TIN MINES AND MIN
— OF —
DARTMOOR
A Photographic Record

Tom Greeves

DEVON BOOKS

This book is dedicated to those who have spent all or part of their lives working on Dartmoor tin mines, and to their families and friends.

First published 1986 by Devon Books
Copyright © Thomas A.P. Greeves 1986
ISBN 0 86114–766–9

British Library Cataloguing in Publication Data
Greeves, Tom
   Tin mines and miners of Dartmoor: a photographic
   record.
   1. Tin mines and mining——England——Dartmoor——
   History——Pictorial works
   I. Title
   338.2′7453′0942353   HD9539.T6D3/

DEVON BOOKS
Publishers to the Devon County Council

Devon Books is a division of A. Wheaton & Co. Ltd who represents:

Design, Editorial & Publicity
Production & Manufacturing
A. Wheaton & Company Ltd, Hennock Road, Exeter, EX2 8RP
Tel: 0392-74121 Telex: 42749 (WHEATN G)
(A. Wheaton & Co. Ltd is a division of Pergamon Press)

Sales & Distribution
Town & Country Books, 24 Priory Avenue, Kingskerswell,
Newton Abbot, TQ12 5AQ Tel: 08047-2690

CONTENTS

PLATES PUBLISHED PREVIOUSLY

Plate 2   Atkinson *et al.* (1978, p.46); Chugg (1975, plate 108); Le Messurier (1966, opposite p.65); Major & Watts (1977, plate 69)

Plate 6   Booker (1967, opposite p.206); Harris (1968, p.143)

Plate 10   Le Messurier (1966, opposite p.65 – detail)

Plate 14   Robins (1984, p.19, plate 5)

Plate 15   Robins (1984, p.20, plate *7a*)

Plate 16   Somers Cocks & Greeves (1983, p.28, plate 18)

Plate 21   Somers Cocks & Greeves (1983, p.53, plate 61 – detail)

Plate 26   Smith (1983, p.48)

Plate 37   Hamilton Jenkin (1974, p.109)

Plate 39   Greeves (1980*a*, p.89, plate 8)

Plate 40   Greeves (1980*a*, p.88, plate 7); *Dartmoor National Park Annual Report*, 1981–2, p.24

Plate 56   Greeves (1985*a*)

Plate 71   Hamilton Jenkin (1974, p.91); Minchinton (1974, p.44)

ABBREVIATIONS

Bodleian   Bodleian Library, Oxford

Cornwall Record Office   Cornwall Record Office, Truro

Devon Record Office   Devon Record Office, Castle Street, Exeter

DuCo Bradninch   Duchy of Cornwall Office, Bowhill, Bradninch, Devon (material referenced to this office was consulted when it was at Princetown)

DuCo London   Duchy of Cornwall Office, 10 Buckingham Gate, London

Grid references   The whole of Dartmoor is covered by the SX prefix. Sites mentioned in the text are best located on the 1:25 000 (2½ in. to the mile) Ordnance Survey Outdoor Leisure Map of Dartmoor, or else on the 1:63 360 (1 in. to the mile) Tourist Map of Dartmoor.

ACKNOWLEDGEMENTS

A major debt is owed to those whose names and addresses are listed below, and I hope this book goes some way towards recognizing it. There are many others with whom I have talked and who are not listed as their information has not been used directly, but I am grateful to them nonetheless. My thanks are due to Tom Pridmore for drawing my attention to plate 24 – an important find. The help of staff in Record Offices has been much appreciated, as has encouragement from a number of sources, including colleagues at work. Some of the most constant support, especially in the early years of my research, has come from my parents and to them I am immensely grateful, as I am to my wife Felicity for bearing with late returns home or long hours of preparation of the final product.

The following provided information or photographs:

Mrs Elsie Bellamy (deceased) and Mr Reginald Bellamy, 30 Staindrop Road, Darlington, Co. Durham

Mrs Bents, Annandale, New Street, Torrington, Devon

Mrs Beatrice Brook, Tor View, Postbridge, Devon

Mrs Burley, Lower Spring, Marytavy, Devon

Mr W. Francis Coaker, Oaklands Caravan Park, Okehampton, Devon

Miss Elsie Chudley, 5 New London, Princetown, Devon (deceased)

Mr and Mrs Pat Dennis, 32 Westabrook Avenue, Ashburton, Devon

Mr W. Dodd, 26 Greatwood Terrace, Topsham, Devon

Mr Nelson Easterbrook, Wheal Lucky, Rundlestone, Princetown, Devon (deceased)

Mr Jim Endacott, Stone Cottage, Frenchbeer, Chagford, Devon (deceased)

Mrs Agnes Evely, Gloucester (consulted at Whitwell, Throwleigh, Devon)

Mr Fred Evely, 1 Walson Cottage, Bow, Crediton, Devon

Mr K. Fox, 19 West Avenue, Exeter, Devon

Mr Sidney French, 82 Ashburton Road, Highweek, Newton Abbot, Devon (deceased)

Mr William A. Grose, 522 Cottonwood Street, Missoula, Montana 59801, U.S.A.

Mr Gordon Hambley, Holcombe, Moretonhampstead, Devon

Mr John Hamlyn, Clitheroe House, St Lawrence Lane, Ashburton, Devon

Mrs Deborah Hannaford, Higher Natsworthy, Widecombe-in-the-Moor, Devon

Mr Peter Hannaford, Sherril, Poundsgate, Newton Abbot, Devon (deceased)

Mr George Hellier, 46 Whitchurch Avenue, Woodwater Lane, Exeter, Devon

Mr Charles Hill, Chagford, Devon

Mr Chris Hill, Lettaford, Moretonhampstead, Devon

Mr Tom Hill, 2 Tolmen, Throwleigh, Devon (deceased)

Mr Frank Hodge, Woolminstone, Crewkerne, Somerset

Mr A. Robin Hood, 31 Church Road, Barton, Torquay, Devon

Miss Annie Leaman, 92 Plymouth Road, Buckfastleigh, Devon (deceased)

Mr Algy May, Rowbrook, Poundsgate, Newton Abbot, Devon (deceased)

Miss Mortimore, Jurston, Chagford, Devon

Mrs Winnie Murch, Hazelwood, Umberleigh, Devon (deceased)

Mrs Polly Osborn, Whitwell, Throwleigh, Devon

Mrs Page, 82 Ashburton Road, Highweek, Newton Abbot, Devon

Mr Michael Perriam, 2 Lonsdale Road, Newton Abbot, Devon

Miss J. Pope, 2 Winslow Court, 100 Fordwych Road, London NW2

Mrs Gertrude Prew, 27 Keyberry Road, Decoy, Newton Abbot, Devon

Mr Martin Radford, 1 Hill House, Worcester Road, Malvern, Worcs.

Mrs Doreen Richards, Little Orchard, Elliston Road, Totland Bay, Isle of Wight

Mr Peter H.G. Richardson, Pentamar, Crosspark, Bridgetown, Totnes, Devon

Lady Sylvia Sayer, Cator, Widecombe-in-the-Moor, Devon

Miss Annie Sleep, Fairholm, Postbridge, Devon (deceased)

Mr Donald Smith, 5 Sharpthorne Crescent, Portslade, Brighton, E. Sussex

Mr Martin Spiller, Eaglehurst, Chagford, Devon (deceased)

Mr Sydney Taylor, Stonehedges, Yelverton, Devon

Mr Garfield Thomas, Bissom Bungalow, Penryn, Cornwall

Mr Simon Timms, 12 North Avenue, Exeter, Devon

Mr Harry Trude, Sunnymead, Postbridge, Devon (deceased)

Mr and Mrs A. Wannacott, Ridgecote, South Zeal, Devon (deceased)

Mr Claude Warne, Quarry Farm, Buckland Tout Saints, Devon

Mr Fernley Warne, Bridge Cottage, Postbridge, Devon (deceased)

Mr Fernley Warne (2), 9 Poundwell Meadow, Modbury, Devon

Mr Frank Warne, 6 Potacre Street, Torrington, Devon (deceased)

Mr Gilbert Warne, 2 Hessary Terrace, Princetown, Devon

Mr Reginald Warne, Martin Farm, Whiddon Down, Okehampton, Devon

Mr Claude Warren, Buckfastleigh, Devon

Mr William Warren, Rosemary Lane, Scorriton, Devon (deceased)

Mrs Emmie Webb, Stannon Lodge, Postbridge, Devon

Mrs Eva Webb, Ferndale, Postbridge, Devon (deceased)

Mr Tom Webb, Stannon Lodge, Postbridge, Devon

Mr Frank Webber, East Week, Throwleigh, Devon

Mrs Irene M. Wellington, Wheal Rose, Smithaleigh, Plympton, Devon

Mr I. Westcott, The Bungalow, Rixhill, Tavistock, Devon

Mrs Ethel White, 9 Cross Street, Northam, Bideford, Devon (deceased)

Mrs Nellie White, Lower Merripit, Postbridge, Devon (deceased)

Mr William Withycombe, Spaders, Postbridge, Devon (deceased)

Mr Ernest Worth, Peat Cot, Princetown, Devon (deceased)

INTRODUCTION

The Dartmoor tin industry has a documented history spanning 800 years, from the mid-twelfth century to the mid-twentieth century. A peak was reached in 1521, when several hundred small tinworks produced 280 tons (285 tonnes) of metallic tin. Disturbance during the Civil War period and other factors then caused the virtual cessation of activity in the mid-seventeenth century. There was a revival in the late seventeenth century especially around Chagford and Tavistock, followed by a decline until the second half of the eighteenth century, when larger mines were opened up with increased amounts of capital from outside the county of Devon. Much of the nineteenth century was a period of relative prosperity with about fifty mines producing tin within the county in the middle of the century. But by about 1900 Hexworthy, Birch Tor & Vitifer and Golden Dagger Mines were the only significant producers on central Dartmoor.

General accounts of Dartmoor tinworking and its field remains can be found in Spooner & Russell (1967), Harris (1968), Booker (1970), Atkinson *et al.* (1978) and Greeves (1980*a*, 1981*a,b*, 1985*a*). Historical accounts of the nineteenth century include Broughton (1971), Hamilton Jenkin (1974, 1981) and Burt *et al.* (1984).

This book is neither a history nor a field guide although both historical and interpretive material will be found within it. It is an attempt to illustrate something of the environment and way of life of the Dartmoor tin miner between sixty and one hundred years ago – as familiar to him and his contemporaries as motorways and supermarkets are to us today. Use is made of contemporary photographs and of oral information from those with direct experience of the mines and their related communities.

The bulk of the book deals with three high moorland mines – Hexworthy, Birch Tor & Vitifer, and Golden Dagger. Although other contemporary mines did exist around the fringes of the moor, the choice of these three has been deliberate, as they had a great impact on moorland society, a good photographic record of them survives, and their sites are easily accessible to the walker. It is hoped that this book will help readers to recreate scenes eighty or more years ago at places where, at best, only low foundations of buildings now survive. At Hexworthy and at Birch Tor & Vitifer the surrounding vegetation has altered very little, but at Golden Dagger there has been dramatic change caused by the planting of Soussons Down with conifers in the late 1940s.

The origin of this book can be traced to two related events which I experienced more than fifteen years ago. The first was in June 1969 when I called at Wheal Lucky Mine House at Rundlestone near Princetown and met Mr Nelson Easterbrook and several of his close relatives who were able to give me previously unrecorded information about the adjoining mine. This made me appreciate vividly the value of talking to people who had always lived within a specific area.

A little more than a year later, in August 1970, Miss Annie Sleep of Postbridge showed me two photographs of Golden Dagger Mine (plates 39 and 42), and from that moment I became aware that there existed previously unpublished photographs of tin miners working on Dartmoor early this century.

Although it was 1969 when I first met Harry Trude, who had worked on the surface at Vitifer and Golden Dagger after the First World War, it was not until February 1974 that I first met someone who had actually worked underground on a Dartmoor tin mine before 1914. This person was Sidney French (1889–1976), formerly of Middle Merripit, Postbridge, who had worked on moorland mines for ten years between 1903 and 1913. In December of the same year I received my first letter from William A. Grose (b. 1886) of Missoula, Montana, U.S.A., whose home was on Hexworthy Mine for several years around the turn of the century. His letters since then have provided much of the detailed information relating to Hexworthy Mine, and I am still in correspondence with him in his ninety-ninth year. In addition, I was able to meet him and his family in America in 1981.

I must also mention Donald Smith, who has done so much to bring to life the last years of Golden Dagger Mine. He was employed there from 1925 to 1930 and fortunately took many photographs, most of which are reproduced here. Besides corresponding with him, I was able to take him to the mine in 1983 and to visit him and his wife in their home at Portslade near Brighton in 1984.

These are some of the highlights of spare-time activity over fifteen years or so which has resulted in this book. There has, of course, been disappointment and frustration too, hearing of photographs and records destroyed or of ex-miners who had died only a year or two before. While people with direct memory of Dartmoor mining are now reduced to a mere handful, I am confident that more photographs remain to be discovered, and I would welcome any information in this respect. In particular, I draw attention to the fact that, before the First World War, a local firm of photographers, Chapman & Sons of Dawlish, published a series of postcards comprising a detailed technical and social record of two of the mines considered here – Birch Tor & Vitifer and Golden Dagger. About a dozen of these are reproduced in this book. However, the serial numbers of the postcards already traced indicate that perhaps two dozen were originally produced. If all of these could be found they would be of enormous interest.

Scores of people who knew or were related to tin miners or who were, in a few cases, tin miners themselves have been talked to, and what is presented here is based on what they have said. Oral history is inherently full of pitfalls owing to the natural failings of memory or the inadequacy of the interviewer to appreciate the significance of what he or she is hearing and thus missing a chance to follow up a vital clue with a subsidiary question. However, the more wide-ranging one's sources the more accurate the picture that can be built up, and it is possible, to a certain extent, to check information from one person against that from another. C.W. Pilkington-Rogers visited Hexworthy Mine in about 1910 and relates a cautionary tale about oral information that every interviewer should note. Being on a working mine he tried to find someone who could explain it to him, but had little success until his 'guide' learnt that he was not about to pick his brains and then write a book. The miner told him:

I've been doing this job for thirty-five years now, and what I don't know about it you needn't go home and worry over. And then they come and want me to tell 'em all I've learnt in a lifetime, so as to know as much as I do without any of the trouble of getting it. I had one down here a few months ago. He brought a list of questions along, and ticked them off as he asked them. 'Is that all right?' he says. 'Yes,' I tells him, and down goes another tick.

When Pilkington-Rogers asked if the information he gave *was* right, the miner replied, 'No, nothing like. But 'twas good enough for 'e.' (Pilkington-Rogers 1930, p.70).

Experience soon teaches an interviewer not to be tactless but it is a delicate art. I myself remain indebted for the warm welcome and interest shown by the great majority of those I have talked to, for whom I was a complete stranger. Wherever possible, information has been checked but there are bound to be more errors in a book of this sort than in a conventional historical or descriptive work. Technical detail can be easily misinterpreted by those unfamiliar with it and personal names will sometimes be misspelt. Any corrections will be gratefully received.

However, despite these failings, for which I take full responsibility, I believe there is a human story here which is worth telling. I hope also that it will encourage others to treat further aspects of the recent history of Dartmoor, such as quarrying or farming activity, in a similar way. Dartmoor, although a wild landscape, is essentially a human resource and its people are a repository of knowledge that cannot be obtained elsewhere.

Tom Greeves
30 Velwell Road
Exeter
August 1985

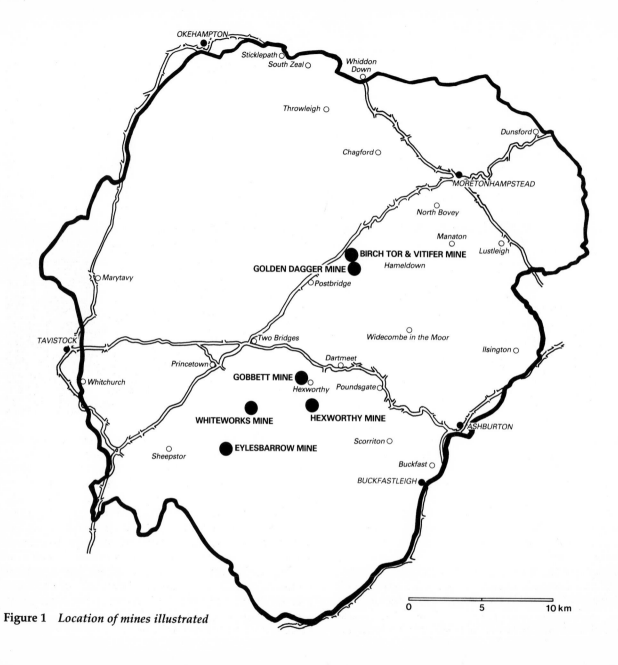

Figure 1 *Location of mines illustrated*

Plate 1 *A group of Dartmoor tin miners in the late nineteenth century*
Photographer: Unknown
Original given to Author by Mrs Emmie Webb

Mrs Emmie Webb of Postbridge, who gave me this photograph in 1974, had always been told that this was a group of tin miners.[1] The tents in the background are curious but it is possible that the photograph was taken in 1873 when there were military training encampments on both Merripit Hill and Water Hill, which lie between Postbridge and the Warren House Inn above Vitifer Mine. Miss Annie Sleep told me that her father Silas was then a lad aged seven and had acted as a newspaper boy for the soldiers while his father, James Sleep, had been volunteer cook.[2] It is not at all unlikely that a group of miners on their way to or from the mine were photographed by a military photographer. Certainly the men are not in military clothes, and the man sitting second from left is holding a drill used for boring in soft ground. The photograph has been shown to people with memories stretching back into the nineteenth century but none of the men has been identified. It is reproduced here for its historic interest as possibly the earliest extant photograph of Dartmoor miners, and in the hope that someone may be able to shed further light on it.

Plate 2 *Stamps water-wheel at Whiteworks Tin Mine,*
1 June 1889
Photographer: R. Burnard　　*Grid reference:* SX 61307083
Original in possession of Lady S. Sayer, reproduced with permission

This is the earliest known extant photograph of tin-mining machinery on Dartmoor. It shows an abandoned water-wheel that had previously been used for stamping, i.e. crushing, tin ore at Whiteworks Mine. The view is looking north-north-west. On the right of the wheel can be seen the vertical lifters for sixteen head of stamps. The stamps axle with its projecting cams is lying out of position in front of them. In the background a launder appears to lead to the wheel but it may in fact be a raised tramroad leading to the stamps as it seems to pass behind the wheel.

Whiteworks Mine was one of the largest Dartmoor tin mines (Hamilton Jenkin 1974, pp.93–4; Greeves 1980b; Burt *et al.* 1984, p.116) but had by this time more or less come to the end of its active life. The wheel shown here is likely to be the one newly purchased, with stamps, in 1869, and due to be sited 160 fathoms (960 ft/293 m) above another wheel.[3] William Crossing (1912, p.106) recorded two wheels here. Ernest Worth (b. 1886) of Peat Cot also remembered seeing two wheels which he described to me as 'sunk into the ground like a ship in water'.[4]

Direct experience of the mine is beyond the reach of living memory but William Francis (Frank) Coaker, who was born at Swincombe in 1906, recalled a story he had heard. A miner and his wife lived at Foxtor Farm. When the woman was expecting her first child it was arranged that she should hang out a white sheet between two elder bushes if she needed help. The day of her labour came but it was foggy and although she hung out the sheet nobody at the mine could see it, so when her husband returned in the evening he found his wife had had the baby without any assistance.[5]

2

Plate 3   *Ruins of tin smelting-house at Eylesbarrow Mine,*
19 January 1889
Photographer: R. Burnard   *Grid reference:* SX 59186765
Original in possession of Lady S. Sayer, reproduced with
permission

This photograph is included here as it is one of the
earliest records of a structure that is now very much
more ruined yet is one of the most important in terms
of the tin-mining history of Dartmoor. It shows the
smelting-house at Eylesbarrow (the last in operation
on Dartmoor) some fifty-eight years after it was last in
commercial production (in 1831), much the same time
interval as that separating us from the final working
of Golden Dagger Mine in about 1930 (see plates
43–69).

The smelting-house was in operation from 1822 to
1831 and contained both reverberatory and blast
furnaces (Cook *et al.* 1974). The main structure seen
here is the reverberatory furnace, while the massive
blocks on the left of the picture formed part of the
framework of the blast furnace. The tin smelter was
called Walter Wellington and during his period of
work some 276 tons (280 tonnes) of tin metal were
produced here.

Notes and References to Plates 1–3

[1] Oral inf., Mrs Emmie Webb, 8 April 1974
[2] Oral inf., Miss Annie Sleep, 24 May 1974
[3] DuCo Bradninch/Letters Received/20 May 1869
[4] Oral inf., Ernest Worth, 18 March 1970
[5] Oral inf., W.F. Coaker, 2 April 1978

HEXWORTHY TIN MINE

An Outline History

This remote mine, situated 1300 ft (400 m) above sea-level and one mile south of the hamlet of Hexworthy, witnessed tinworking activity over hundreds of years. Workings on Dry Lake (SX 661708) were mentioned in 1240 (Somers Cocks 1970, p.279), and several references exist to tinworks in the vicinity in the sixteenth and early seventeenth centuries. These include 'Welaby' (SX 659700), a tinwork in which John Langadon of Staverton held a share in 1542,[1] and 'Scurr' (SX 647706), mentioned in both 1569 and the early seventeenth century.[2]

Many extensive openwork gullies survive in the vicinity of Hensroost (SX 651711) and Hooten Wheals (SX 656707) and are evidence of large-scale opencast lode mining in the late medieval period. However, it is only from the nineteenth century that substantial documentation survives.

In October 1845 William Treble, a miner of Hexworthy, was granted by the Duchy of Cornwall a licence for an area around Skir Gut and Hensroost to work for tin.[3] A few years later, in 1849, Henry and William Choake of Buckfastleigh obtained a licence for one year to work a mine called Wheal Unity comprising the area around what is now known as Hooten Wheals.[4] From 1852, when a new licence was granted to George Bennetts, a mining engineer from Ilsington,[5] the mine was mostly known as Hensroost or Hexworthy. Bennetts worked it in conjunction with Ringleshutes Mine (SX 675697) under the title 'The Holm Moor and Hen's Roost United Mines'.[6]

Four men were employed at Hensroost in January 1854, clearing out an ancient adit.[7]

Little is then known of the mine's history for some thirty years, until the late 1880s, when a series of leases was granted by the Duchy of Cornwall to Edward Mogridge and others.[8] In December 1889 the road to the mine was being cut through a newtake (enclosed moorland), which displeased John Chaffe, a local farmer.[9]

On 20 March 1890 a lease for twenty-one years from 1 January 1890 was granted to Edward Mogridge and to John and Robert Taylor, mining engineers.[10] Fifty-nine men were employed on the mine in 1891 (Burt et al. 1984, p.73) and tin of the finest quality was produced (Barton 1967, p.190, note). However, the prosperity did not last and on 5 December 1895 an auction of all machinery and materials was advertised. These included '20 iron beds, with mattresses, palliasses, pillows, sheets, blankets and counterpanes'.[11] The lease was terminated on 1 January 1896 after only six years of operation.[12]

But the mine was soon reactivated under Edward Herbert Bayldon of Dawlish, who obtained a succession of leases from the Duchy of Cornwall from 1896 onwards.[13] Several of these were in partnership with Frederick Pine Theophilus Struben of Torquay, who also owned Spitchwick Manor in the parish of Widecombe. This is the period remembered by William Grose (b.1886), whose father, Ambrose, was

4

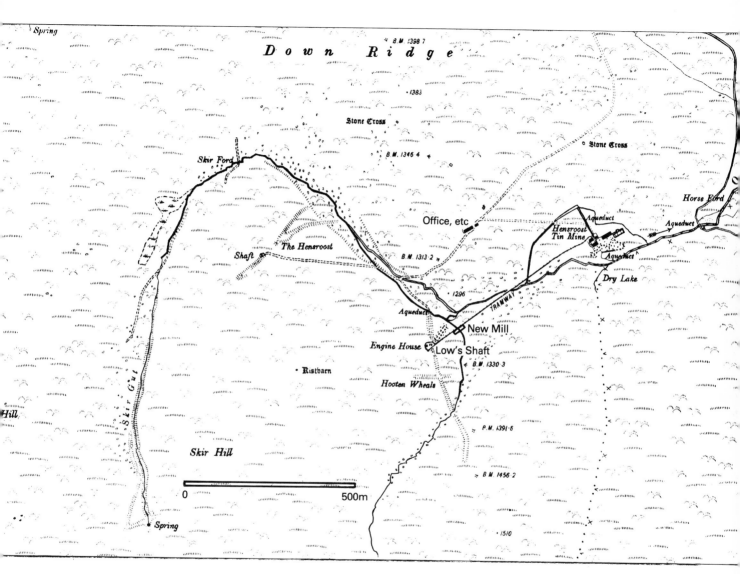

Figure 2 *Map of Hexworthy Tin Mine. Based on Ordnance Survey 2nd edition 6 in., 1906, Sheet 107 SE (surveyed 1883–4; revised 1904), with additions*

5

appointed agent to the mine by Mr Bayldon. He recalls Struben and his son visiting the mine in about 1900:

One day at Hexworthy two horsemen came riding up to the house, a gentleman and his son, the son about my age or a little younger and riding a pony. Both Horse and Pony were high class horses. Both [the men] were perfectly attired in riding clothes. It was Mr Struben and his son. Father was there and they went into the house. A few minutes later Father came out to me and said 'Show this young gentleman over the mine', which I did. He told me his name at the start – 'My name is Lester Frederick Struben' – in the language of the young aristocrat, and turned out to be a very agreeable young gentleman … I remember young Struben telling me he was soon to enter one of the famous Public Schools – Harrow, Winchester or Rugby, I forget which.[14]

Bayldon was granted a twenty-one year lease from 17 January 1900 but this was terminated, as Lord Armstrong and others were granted a new twenty-one year lease from 26 July 1905 which heralded the last phase of work on the mine and the installation of new machinery.[15] Forty-five men were employed in 1908, during which year nearly £4200 worth of tin was produced (Burt *et al.* 1984, p.73). The last known leases were granted from 29 September 1914 for thirty years, to Harry Maconochie, with an additional piece of ground for twenty-six years from 29 September 1918.[16]

Thirteen and a half tons of black tin were produced in 1915–16 (Hamilton Jenkin 1974, p.101). The last underground work was carried out by a team headed by an Australian miner in the summer of 1919. A storm in 1920 caused serious flooding of the mine, and although proposals were made in 1925 to re-open it, nothing further was done.[17] During the Second World War many of the structures were severely damaged during training by American forces.

Published accounts of the mine can be found in Reid *et al.* (1912), Dines (1956, p.729), Le Messurier (1966, pp.64–6), Harris (1968, pp.50–52), Richardson (1972, 1973), Hamilton Jenkin (1974, pp.99–101), Atkinson *et al.* (1978, pp.32–4), Hemery (1983, p.420) and Burt *et al.* (1984, p.73).

Notes and References to Hexworthy Tin Mine

[1] Devon Record Office 50/11/40/1
[2] Devon Record Office DD 3815; 46/1/3/9
[3] DuCo London/Inrolment Book Vol.7, p.141
[4] DuCo London/Mineral Grants Vol.1, 21 May 1849; Inrolment Book Vol.19, p.253
[5] DuCo London/Mineral Grants Vol.1
[6] *Mining Journal* 21 January 1854
[7] *Idem*
[8] DuCo London/Mineral Grants Vol.1
[9] DuCo Bradninch/Letters Received/28 Dec. 1889
[10] DuCo London/Mineral Grants Vol.1
[11] Photocopy of newspaper advertisement in possession of Author (*ex* Westcountry Studies Library, Exeter)
[12] DuCo London/Mineral Grants Vol.1
[13] *Idem*
[14] W.A. Grose *in litt.*, 11 Dec. 1977
[15] DuCo London/Mineral Grants Vol.1
[16] *Idem*
[17] Cornwall Record Office/TL 104/31

Plate 4 *Water-wheel opposite Dry Lake, c.1905. View looking west-north-west*
Photographer: Unknown   *Grid reference:* SX 66027109
Copy provided by M. Radford, 1974

The large water-wheel was 45 ft (13.7 m) in diameter and 5 ft (1.5 m) wide.[1] A sense of scale is provided by a human figure which is just visible standing against the centre of wheel. Before the turbine was constructed at Saddle Bridge in 1907 to produce electricity for the mine (see plate 7), this wheel was the power source for all stamping, i.e. crushing, operations. On the right of the picture is the stamps axle for a set of twelve Cornish stamps which had by this time been removed. On the opposite side of the wheel are the slim vertical lifters for a set of sixteen Californian stamps – an improvement on the Cornish variety as they twisted as they fell, which increased their pulverizing effect. These came from Terras Mine, St Stephen, near St Austell in Cornwall, in about 1900[2] and were installed by Ambrose Grose, who was captain of Hexworthy Mine. The stamps could be worked day and night throughout the winter, when water was plentiful, but in summer water was often in short supply and was stored in a reservoir a short distance above the wheel. The reservoir provided enough water to work the stamps continuously for about two hours.[3]

Below the wheel was the dressing-floor (not visible in the photograph). The tin dresser in about 1900 was Dicky Jones from Buckfastleigh and about eight men worked with him. In hot weather it became very dusty and William Grose remembers Dicky Jones saying to him once, 'Us be stiffled doon yer.'[4] The small shed by the wheel was where the men could eat or keep their lunches.[5]

In about 1905 pumping rods were also attached to the wheel (Richardson 1972). These can be seen supported on flanged wheels and wooden trestles and leading out of the picture and to the left. They led to Low's Shaft, some 550 m further up the valley (see plate 11).

The wheel is a pitchback wheel. The vertical box-like structure attached to the launder and set behind the wheel is known as a 'downright hatch' and was a means of turning water off the wheel. It was controlled by a wire. The embankment behind the shed was the end of a self-acting gravity tramroad that brought ore from the shaft to the stamps to be crushed. It consisted of a double track with a drum at the top, a brake for control, and a wire rope attached to the wagons. A full wagon hauled up an empty one.[6]

On the horizon in the background can be seen several buildings. The largest, on the left, was the mine captain's house and mine office. Its ruins can be seen today at SX 65667112. William Grose (b. 1886), who was put on the pay-roll of the mine in the spring of 1901 as 'utility boy', described it as follows:

It was a four room house, two down and two bedrooms. The one at the extreme left was our sitting room and also used as the office, the other our living room or kitchen. Not too much room but well built and comfortable and fairly large rooms. When the Bayldons came they had lunch in the sitting room and the door was closed. They invariably left part of a bottle of good wine behind, sometimes a little and sometimes half full . . . The two upstairs rooms were furnished with beds when we went there . . . The furniture of the house [i.e. office] was office furniture – a desk, table, a panelled wall, three windows, fireplace, grate, and also we found there a set of assayer's scales for weighing tin . . . It was a substantially built house and quite warm during the cold winter days on Dartmoor and we were, shall we say, more or less comfortable there during the storms and blizzards of the Dartmoor winter and the heat of its summer.[7]

The two left-hand chimneys in the photograph belonged to the dwelling-house. The right-hand chimney was for the 'Dry' where the underground clothes were dried. The Dry was on the ground floor and consisted of a long steel tube about two-thirds full of water with a firebox one end and the gases passing underneath its entire length. The wet clothes were draped over it and on racks overhead for drying. William Grose describes it in more detail and also an improvement his father made to it:

It was not really a 'boiler' but a water heater, about 12 feet long and 3 ft 6 in or 4 feet in diameter. Father conceived the idea of putting a tube down through the middle of it and arrange for the fire and gases to go through the tube and not under the boiler, thus this inner tube would be entirely surrounded by water and would heat faster. Care had to be taken, and was, that evaporation would be faster and an adequate vent was installed and the water level above the tube inspected which was my job. It had to be not less than six inches above the tube.[8]

The alterations were carried out in the summer so that, it was hoped, the clothes could be dried naturally, but inevitably some days it was rainy or cool and 'often the miners went underground with wet clothes'. William Grose remembers that most took it in good humour, knowing things would improve when the work was completed, but one miner from Buckfastleigh complained bitterly:

One day going underground in damp clothes he said (I heard him say it), 'What the hell are things coming to? If my old woman knowed that I was going to work in wet clothes like this, er'd piss 'erself!'[9]

Above the Dry was a dormitory with twelve or fourteen beds in two rows, where the men slept who stayed for the week from Monday to Saturday midday. In about 1900 at least eight men came from Buckfastleigh. Others came from Scorriton, Ashburton, Lustleigh, Princetown and Postbridge, besides Hexworthy itself. Joe Creber and his older brother and a man called Jack Dodds came from Marytavy, eleven miles distant as the crow flies. 'They came Monday morning, they walked from Marytavy to Hexworthy. Right across, they came across the moor, you know, in all weathers.' Later they went mining in India, where they met Ambrose Grose again.[10]

Attached to the right-hand end of the main building is the blacksmith's shop where Jim Chapman of Buckfastleigh worked, much of his time being spent in drill sharpening. The middle building on the horizon was the carpenter's shop (SX 65707113). This is where old Tommy Johns of Lustleigh was employed (see plate 18). The building on the right was known as the Iron House, being of wood covered with galvanized iron. Some men slept here but it was mostly used as a place where the men had their meals or stayed when not working on a shift.[11] Its site is at SX 65727118.

Although the mine was, in William Grose's words, 'a lonely wild place', weekly groceries were delivered by Bolts of Princetown. 'Mother sent them a grocery list on Saturdays by the Postman and a delivery van came every Tuesday with them. Also, the miners bought from the same source.'[12] Sidney French (b. 1889) of Middle Merripit, Postbridge, was employed for several months at Hexworthy before the First World War when it was being worked jointly with Golden Dagger. He walked from Postbridge carrying basic food for the week with him, and stayed on the mine. The food would include pasties and boiled season pudding wrapped in a cloth. A man would be delegated to heat up the food for the men coming up from underground.

Another common item of food among miners was salted dried cod known as 'toregg'. Annie Sleep recalled that 'when they were down Hexworthy at the mines down there they used to soak it in the leat, and somebody else's cats got the wise to that – they used to come and take it out again.'[13]

Plate 5   *Water-wheel opposite Dry Lake, August 1917, viewed from the north-east*
Photographer: M. Spiller   *Grid reference:* SX 66027109
Original loaned by M. Spiller

The mine was abandoned at this time but the photograph shows well the launder, the 'downright hatch' and the moorland setting of the wheel. The woman in the photograph is the photographer's mother, Mrs Spiller.

Plate 6 *Water-wheel opposite Dry Lake, c.1918, viewed from the west*
Photographer: Unknown   *Grid reference:* SX 66027109
Original loaned by Mrs Irene M. Wellington

By the time this photograph was taken the Californian stamps had been removed (from the foreground). Just visible in the background on the right is part of the line of pumping rods taken off the opposite side of the wheel. In the winter of 1920 a storm demolished the launder carrying water to the wheel. This automatically stopped the pumping and caused the head of the shaft to collapse thereby flooding the mine.[14]

The wheel was still *in situ* in August 1934 but had gone by the following year.[15] However, the pit still remains and is one of the most impressive on the moor. In 1980 the Dartmoor National Park Authority took steps to prevent its collapse, by shoring it up with massive timbers.

Plate 7 *Turbine House at Saddle Bridge, c.1910*
Photographer: J. Spencer   *Grid reference:* SX 66427192
Original in possession of Lady S. Sayer, reproduced with permission

This was situated just above Saddle Bridge on the left bank of the O Brook. The bridge can be seen on the right.

The building housed a Pelton wheel which drove a dynamo generating 140 h.p. This provided power for the stamps, dressing-floors, hoist and lighting (Reid *et al.* 1912, p.74). Water for the wheel was taken off the old Wheal Emma Leat in a large-diameter pipe which was reduced to a nozzle of very small diameter before the water struck the cups of the wheel. This created a very powerful jet – 'Bunny' Spiller recalled that a walking-stick would bounce off it.[16] This modern plant was installed in 1907.[17]

10

Plate 8 *Miners underground at Hexworthy Mine, c.1910*
Photographer: Unknown   *Grid reference:* SX 656708 (approx.)
Copy provided by A. Robin Hood, 1985

This is the only photograph yet traced which shows working miners at Hexworthy. It is a view inside a shaft, possibly Low's, but perhaps more likely to be an air shaft. A ladder can be seen in the background as can part of a pipe which probably took compressed air down the shaft. None of the men has been identified. The photograph was given to A. R. Hood by J. Cleave, formerly of the Forest Inn, Hexworthy.

Plate 9 *General view of the engine house, Low's Shaft, tramroad and dressing-floors, c.1915, viewed from the north*
Photographer: Miss May   *Grid reference:* SX 656708
Original loaned by Algy May, 1976

All the structures shown here relate to the refurbishment of the mine in 1907.[18] William Grose, who left the mine in 1903, was unable to recognize anything in the picture, although his father had himself put up a headframe over Low's Shaft, and a smaller engine house for a steam hoist and steam pump.[19]

The gantry supporting the tramroad leading from the shaft to the dressing-floors or 'New Mill' can be seen. By 1912 the mill contained ten electrically driven stamps besides three hydraulic classifiers, two Wilfley tables and a revolving Wilfley slime table (Reid *et al.* 1912, p.74). According to Frank Warne (b. 1901) the new engine house or 'Power House' contained an air compressor, winding gear and electrically operated pumps.[20]

Jack Warne (1875–1956) of Postbridge, brother to Freddy, Harry and William, was working as a miner at Hexworthy when William Grose was there *c.* 1900 and later became captain of the mine, in about 1910.[21] His recollections of mining there were printed with his obituary notice in the *Tavistock Times* of 12 October 1956:

I started myself in the mine when I was 14 years of age. And I walked more than seven miles to work. Every Monday morning I walked to Hexworthy tin mine, beyond the Forest Inn. When I started to work in Hexworthy Mine there were many of us who used to walk miles to work Monday mornings. We would set off at five o'clock and, mark this, we would take our week's food with us. I used to take four to five pasties along with me. They would last me until Thursday. Then I always had some season pudding for Friday and, of course, on the Saturday we used to set off for home again. Certainly we were able to warm the grub up again. I have taken bacon and eggs and dried fish with me, the point being that I could not get food there. Where could we buy it? Don't think I had the hardest job of all the miners. Far from it. Why a man called Inglewood used to walk in every Monday, and back home on Saturday, from South Zeal, and he brought his food with him, too. At one time there were 25 to 30 men who came from Mary Tavy. But for them there was a man called Littlejohns who had a donkey and cart and he used to bring food out to the Mary Tavy men, all of whom at one time had worked at the Friendship Mine, which had closed down. How did we manage about the cooking? Well, when I went first we had our own saucepans and frying pans, otherwise there would have been a terrible mix-up.

We used to start work at seven in the morning and leave off at two o'clock if we were on the morning shift and from two to ten if we were on the second shift. No matter how far we had to walk to work Monday mornings we had to be there on the dot at seven. I remember one time my boss said to me: 'John, you are a bit late this morning.' I said, 'Well, you know where I have had to come from this morning.' He said, 'Yes, I know. Don't come it too often. Time and tide wait for no man.' And I had left home between four and five that morning! We had to get there. Times are different today. The youngsters of today won't believe me when I tell 'em.

Plate 10 *General view of the site of Low's Shaft, the engine house and the dressing-floors, 1941*
Photographer: S. Taylor   *Grid reference:* SX 656708
Original in possession of S. Taylor, reproduced with permission

Twenty-five years after the scene in plate 9, the site was ruined and deserted, as shown here.

Plate 11 *Low's Shaft and engine house, c.1914, viewed from the east*
Photographer: G. W. A. Shepherd *Grid reference:* SX 65587080
Copy provided by A. Robin Hood, 1985

Compare this photograph with plate 9, where the headframe and the engine house can be seen on the right. The rails in the foreground lead to the waste tips and the New Mill or dressing-floors. The line of pumping rods from the water-wheel opposite Dry Lake can be seen approaching the shaft on the right.

From about 1900 onwards, this was the only shaft worked at Hexworthy Mine. In September 1915 it was recorded as being 316 ft (96.3 m) deep.[22]

A magazine recorded the part played by Freddy Warne (born *c.*1877) in this work:

Eventually only Hexworthy was left, with good tin coming out of the 305 ft shaft which Mr Warne helped to sink in 1913. 'There's still a lot of loose tin down there today', he said. 'Hexworthy is the most beautiful little mine in Devon, and if anyone wanted to start mining tomorrow, that's where I'd tell them to start digging. I fixed the last blast down there on the day it closed, and we didn't gather that day's tin up so we could always say that there's still tin on Dartmoor.'[23]

Plate 12 *Headframe over Low's Shaft, August 1917*
Photographer: M. Spiller   *Grid reference:* SX 65577081
Original loaned by M. Spiller

This photograph was taken by Martin 'Bunny' Spiller at the age of fifteen with a camera that cost five shillings.[24]

Plate 13 *View inside the New Mill and dressing-floors, c.1920 (?)*
Photographer: Unknown   *Grid reference:* SX 65657085
Original loaned by M. Perriam, 1982

This photograph appears to have been taken soon after the mill was abandoned, or just possibly while it was still under construction. The vertical lifters of some of the Californian stamps can be seen on the extreme left.

Note the cement facing and back retaining wall as these can still be identified on site today (see Harris 1968, p.71, bottom plate).

Plate 14 *Winding gear at Low's Shaft, 22 August 1934*
Photographer: P. H. G. Richardson
Grid reference: SX 65557081
Negative loaned by P. H. G. Richardson

The mine had been totally abandoned for at least ten years by the time this photograph was taken. It shows the remains of the controls for the electrically powered winding gear, and also the cable, inside the engine house at Low's Shaft.[25]

Plate 15 *View eastwards over Low's Shaft, 14 August 1938*
Photographer: P. H. G. Richardson *Grid reference:* SX 656708
Negative loaned by P. H. G. Richardson

This view looking down the O Brook shows the mine in an advanced state of decay. Peter Richardson recorded, 'Only the buddle foundations now remain, with one or two odd fragments of machinery. The timberwork of the stamps has been destroyed by fire, and the building housing them has collapsed.'[26]

Plate 16 *Cottages at Gobbett Mine, 1905*

Photographer: R. Burnard   *Grid reference:* SX 64697282
Original in possession of Lady S. Sayer, reproduced with permission

The view is looking northwards to Sherberton Farm and Bellever Tor. The cottages in the foreground comprised two homes. In one lived Mr Halfyard, carpenter and builder to the Duchy of Cornwall. In the other lived Mr James Chudley, tin miner, and his family. He was at this time employed on surface work at Hexworthy Mine, one mile to the south-east (see plate 17).[27] The cottages have now been demolished but were originally built as part of Gobbett Tin Mine, which finally ceased working about one hundred years ago.

Mrs Gertrude Prew (née Chudley), who was born here in 1892, remembers that conditions were very crowded and that when a baby sister died aged nine months the body was put 'in the window' as there was no room for it elsewhere.[28]

16

Plate 17 *James Chudley at Swincombe Farm*
Photographer: Mrs G. Prew (née Chudley)
Grid reference: SX 639725
Original loaned by Mrs G. Prew

Born in 1860, James Chudley was working as a farm labourer at Dunsford in about 1890 when he was attracted to move to Gobbett (plate 16) by the higher wages offered at Hexworthy Mine.[29] William Grose remembers him as 'pithead man and general help' on the mine in about 1900.[30] His wife did not want him to work underground so he stayed on the surface earning £1 a week.[31] His sons, Fred and William, both worked on the dressing-floors at Hexworthy, opposite Dry Lake.[32] His daughter, Mrs Gertrude Prew, recalls that he cut turf (peat) for Captain Grose one year.[33] Another task he did was to carry the laundry from the mine home to his wife to wash.[34]

He also worked part-time at Sherberton Farm[35] and eventually moved in 1913 to Swincombe Farm, which was newly built. He finally gave up work at Hexworthy Mine in 1914 and remained on his farm thereafter.[36] He died in about 1950 aged over ninety.[37]

Plate 18 *Thomas Johns, mine carpenter*
Photographer: Unknown
Copy provided by Mrs Doreen Richards

The mine carpenter at Hexworthy in about 1900 was Thomas Johns and he is seen here, holding a saw, at Owlacombe Mine near Ashburton in about 1908.

William Grose (b. 1886) worked with him at Hexworthy and remembers him as a good carpenter, especially in the manufacture of small-diameter buddle water-wheels.[38] Although his home was at Lustleigh when he was employed at Hexworthy, he originally came from Porthleven in Cornwall, where he was born in about 1840. He is known to have been a ship's carpenter but spent much of his life working on Devon mines. In the late 1870s he was at Steeperton Tor tin mine on northern Dartmoor (Greeves 1985*b*) and in about 1890 was at Atlas Mine, Ilsington. He married Rosina Kitto (b. 1844), and died in March 1917.[39] He provides a good example of the mobility of those working in mines.

Plate 19 *William A. Grose and his wife Bessie (née Fine) at their home, 522 Cottonwood Street, Missoula, Montana, U.S.A., August 1981*

Photographer: Author

William Grose was born on 8 November 1886 at Ivy Cottage, St Stephen in Brannel, near St Austell, Cornwall. His father was Ambrose John Grose, a mining man all his life, and his paternal grandfather was Captain William A. Grose, who had moved from Cornwall to Ilsington on the south-east side of Dartmoor to work mines there.

William Grose spent most of his early years in Cornwall and went to school in St Stephen. His father was absent for much of the 1890s, mining in Michigan and West Africa, and sending money back to his family. In 1898 Ambrose Grose took over responsibility for Hexworthy Mine on behalf of Mr E. H. Bayldon of Dawlish, who held a lease of the mine from the Duchy of Cornwall. His wife and son, William, joined him there and William was put on the pay-roll of the mine in 1901. He worked with his father as messenger boy and also was responsible for handing out dynamite and explosives to the miners. In 1902 he began a five-and-a-half-year apprenticeship with Willcocks & Son, engineers of Buckfastleigh, returning home to Hexworthy at the week-ends. The family moved to Owlacombe Mine near Ashburton in late 1903. From 1908 to 1921 William Grose was employed by Holman Bros of Camborne, Cornwall, and in 1921 he emigrated to America, where he has lived ever since.

Bessie Grose, although born in America, had Cornish parents called Fine. Both her father and her grandfather came from Camborne and were connected with mines there. She spent about ten years of her childhood in Cornwall but returned to America towards the end of the First World War.[40]

Notes and References to Plates 4–19

1. W. A. Grose *in litt.*, 11 June 1976
2. Oral inf., W. A. Grose, 1 Aug. 1981
3. Oral inf., W. A. Grose, 2 Aug. 1981
4. *Idem*
5. W. A. Grose *in litt.*, 11 June 1976
6. Oral inf., W. A. Grose, 1 Aug. 1981 and 3 Aug. 1981 (tape), and *in litt.*, 11 June 1976
7. W. A. Grose *in litt.* rec'd Nov. 1976
8. *Idem*
9. *Idem*
10. W. A. Grose *in litt.*, 11 June 1976, and oral inf., 3 Aug. 1981 (tape)
11. W. A. Grose *in litt.* rec'd Nov. 1976 and 11 June 1976, and oral inf., 3 Aug. 1981 (tape)
12. W. A. Grose *in litt.* rec'd Nov. 1976
13. Oral inf., Sidney French, 4 Feb. 1974 (tape); Miss Annie Sleep, 10 Aug. 1970 (tape)
14. Cornwall Record Office/TL 104/31 – the Author is indebted to P. H. G. Richardson for providing him with a copy of this document
15. Private papers in possession of P. H. G. Richardson, 'Recent Information Vol. I 1927–1952'
16. Oral inf., M. Spiller, 16 Dec. 1980
17. Cornwall Record Office/TL 104/31
18. *Idem*
19. W. A. Grose *in litt.*, Sept. 1977
20. Oral inf., Frank Warne, 6 Nov. 1976
21. Oral inf., Fernley Warne, 11 Sept. 1970; W. A. Grose *in litt.*, 19 March 1976
22. Cornwall Record Office/TL 104/31
23. The cutting (? from *Sporting Life*) was shown to the Author by Fernley Warne, 11 Sept. 1970, and was copied into the Author's notebook
24. Oral inf., M. Spiller, 16 Dec. 1980
25. Private papers in possession of P. H. G. Richardson, 'Recent Information Vol. I 1927–1952'
26. *Idem*
27. Oral inf., Mrs G. Prew (née Chudley), 9 July 1977 and 3 Oct. 1984
28. Oral inf., Mrs G. Prew, 3 Oct. 1984
29. Oral inf., Mrs G. Prew, 9 July 1977
30. W. A. Grose *in litt.*, 19 March 1976
31. Oral inf., Mrs G. Prew, 3 Oct. 1984
32. W. A. Grose *in litt.*, 19 March 1976
33. Oral inf., Mrs G. Prew, 3 Oct. 1984
34. W. A. Grose *in litt.* rec'd Nov. 1976
35. Oral inf., P. Hannaford, 7 Dec. 1975
36. Oral inf., Miss Elsie Chudley, 10 May 1977
37. Oral inf., Mrs G. Prew, 23 Oct. 1979 (tape)
38. W. A. Grose *in litt.*, Sept. 1977, Feb. 1978 and 26 Dec. 1984
39. Mrs D. Richards (née Johns) *in litt.*, 9 Nov. 1984
40. Information relating to plate 19 is taken from letters from and conversations with W. A. Grose, 1974–1984, and oral information from Mr and Mrs Pat Dennis, 17 June 1974

Birch Tor & Vitifer Tin Mine

An Outline History

An area of open moorland covering approximately three-quarters of a square mile (2 sq.km) and lying south of Bennett's Cross (SX 681817) was once the scene of some of the most extensive tinworking activity on Dartmoor, dating from the medieval period if not before. Here are visible the vast man-made gullies where lode ore was exploited by opencast methods and later by shaft mining, and in the valleys are the waste heaps of alluvial workings, or streamworks. Among all these remains lie the ruined structures associated with mining – wheelpits, dwelling-houses, blacksmiths' shops, etc.

The later history of the mine has been relatively well studied, especially by Broughton (1968/9, 1971) and Hamilton Jenkin (1974, pp. 101–105). Birch Tor and Vitifer are, strictly speaking, two separate mines, with Vitifer forming the west side of the Redwater valley in North Bovey parish, and Birch Tor the east side, but for most of their working lives they were operated together and are thus grouped together here. Dartmoor people most commonly pronounce Vitifer as 'Vytifer' though occasionally 'Vittifer' is heard.

Early documentary references as yet elude us, and the first definite records of tinworking date from the mid-eighteenth century. 'Vitifer Mine' was recorded in 1750 (Hemery 1983, p.614) and 'Burch Tor Bounds' in 1757.[1]

In the 1780s Vitifer was being successfully worked by the Dartmoor Mining & Smelting Company.[2] The mine was visited by Charles Hatchett in 1796, when he recorded that forty men were employed and that there were thirteen shafts (Raistrick 1967, p.21). The Revd John Swete paid a visit a year or two later and noted that there was a pumping water-wheel 36 ft (11 m) in diameter and an adit driven for half a mile up the valley which had taken nearly four years to complete.[3] No smelting of tin was done on the mine but ore was sent to a smelting-house on the banks of the River Tamar[4] and also to Calenick Smelting House near Truro in Cornwall.[5] In the 1820s ore was sent to Eylesbarrow Mine (plate 3) in the parish of Sheepstor to be smelted (Hamilton Jenkin 1974, p.102).

The mine continued to be prosperous throughout much of the early nineteenth century. In 1834 it was 'large and profitable' and being worked by a Captain John Paull.[6] However, conditions were notoriously bad for the employees, who numbered 117 in 1838, including women and children (Collins 1912). In 1835 it was stated that 'the accommodation afforded . . . is so wretched that they are obliged to succeed each other in the same bed, which is thus in use throughout the 24 hours'.[7] To make matters worse the mine had a reputation as a refuge for those escaping the law for petty offences (Hamilton Jenkin 1974, p.103). The vicar of Widecombe, the Revd J. H. Mason, wrote that 'Dartmoor has been fitly called the Botany Bay for Miners'.[8] Conditions underground were no better. William Hosking, who worked at Birch Tor in the mid-1830s, described the mine as follows:

'It was a very rich mine when I worked there, and they had but one shaft, and in the summer time the air was

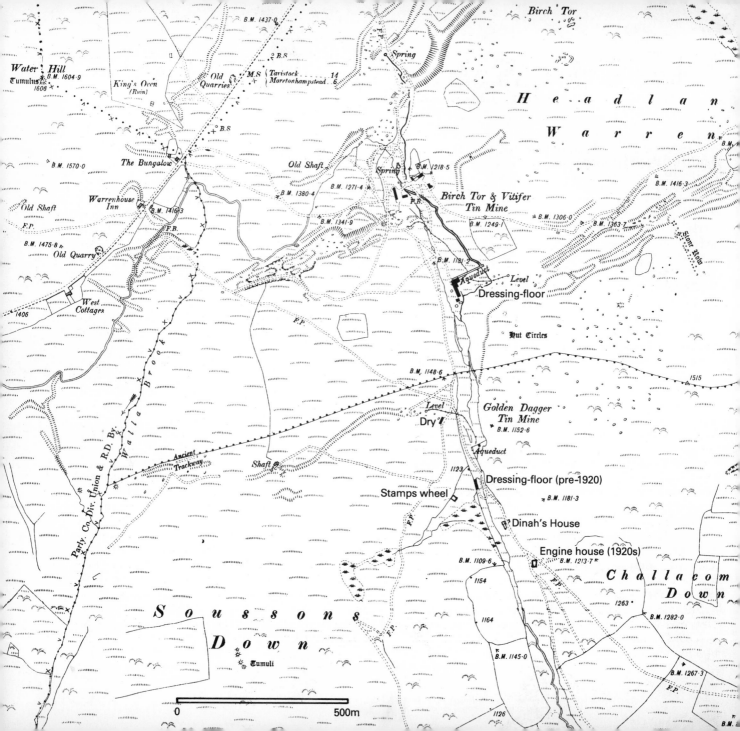

Birch Tor

B.M. 1437·0

H e a d l a n

W a r r e n

Spring

Water Hill
Tumulus
B.M. 1604·9
1606

King's Oven
(Ruin)

Old
Quarries

M.S.   Tavistock   14
       Moretonhampstead 6

B.S.

B.S.

B.M. 1570·0

The Bungalow

B.M. 1218·5

Old Shaft

Spring

B.M. 1271·4

Birch Tor & Vitifer
Tin Mine

Old Shaft
F.P.

Warrenhouse
Inn

B.M. 1416·3

B.M. 1380·4

B.M. 1306·0

B.M. 1363·7

B.M. 1416·3

Stone Row

F.B.

B.M. 1341·9

B.M. 1249·1

B.M. 1475·8

Old Quarry

B.M. 1181·2

Aqueduct

Level

Dressing-floor

West
Cottages

1406

F.P.

Hut Circles

Walla Brook

B.M. 1148·6

1515

Level

Dry

Golden Dagger
Tin Mine

B.M. 1152·6

Parly. Co. Div. Union & R.D. By.

Ancient
Trackway

Shaft

Aqueduct

1123

Dressing-floor (pre-1920)

Stamps wheel

B.M. 1181·3

Dinah's House

Engine house (1920s)

B.M. 1109·6

B.M. 1213·7

C h a l l a c o m

D o w n

1154

1263

1164

B.M. 1282·0

S o u s s o n s

D o w n

Tumuli

1145·0

1126

B.M. 1267·3

F.P.

0   500m

Figure 3 *Map of Birch Tor & Vitifer and Golden Dagger Tin Mines. Based on Ordnance Survey 2nd edition 6 in., 1906, Sheets 99 NE and 99 SE (surveyed 1883–4; revised 1904), with additions*

very bad. I have seen the time when we could not carry in a light below the six fathoms from the surface in some parts of the season, and I being in an end I have seen my comrade in that end working, and I have gone back and have sat down, and I could see the shadow of the man but not the man; that was caused by the cold damp; and if a man put some tobacco in his pipe and took the candle to smoke, directly he took away the candle from the tobacco he could not draw any more smoke, the pipe would go out . . . It killed scores of miners.[9]

Not more than about twenty men were employed throughout the mid-1850s,[10] but the early 1860s saw a considerable revival with about 150 people employed above and below ground in 1863.[11] A peak of production was reached in 1864 with 150 tons (152 tonnes) of black tin being sold for £9687 (Burt *et al.* 1984, p.15).

By 1870 there were still 102 persons employed (Williams 1870, p.81) but twelve years later, in 1882, the sett was 'totally abandoned'.[12] Moses Bawden, who had been associated with the mine since the 1860s, obtained a lease of the sett from the Duchy of Cornwall for thirty-one years from 29 September 1887[13] and the mine remained under his management at mostly a very low level of activity until 1903, when the lease was surrendered. A new lease was granted to W. Phelips and W. Padfield for thirty-one years from 29 September 1903,[14] and from then until 1913 an average of twenty-two miners were employed each year (Burt *et al.* 1984, p.16).

Many families, several from outside Dartmoor, became involved in the mine at this time. John Thomas (*c.* 1865 to *c.* 1946), born at Rosewarne Downs, Camborne, the son of a farmer, had worked in a silver mine in Montana, U.S.A. in his late teens and also in South Africa. His son Garfield (b. 1895) recalled how his father came to be working at Birch Tor & Vitifer Mine in about 1904:

At Redruth fair one Whit Saturday my father met Capt. Bennetts who was home for a few days holiday from Birch Tor mine where Capt. Bennetts was the Manager. Of course they had a long talk about the mine and Capt. Bennetts said he wanted someone like my father to straighten things up and get going and he persuaded my father to go back with him for a week or two. This he did and stayed 3 years. During that time my father lived with Capt. Bennetts in a Cottage on the mine and my mother and me spent several Holidays up there . . . We stayed several times with Miss Leaman's familly at Dury Farm . . . I remember there was a sort of wood and galvanised Bunk House on the end of the Cottage where several of the mine workers eat and sleapt. There were 3 or 4 miners who used to come up from Gunnislake they would come up Monday mornings by pony and trap and go home for week ends. There was one named Kemp I think who gave my father a lot of trouble. There was a wood Bungalow on the mine where Mr. & Mrs. Woolcock [i.e. Willcocks] and son Carberry lived. Mr. Woolcock was the Managering Director of the mine and the Chairman Director a Mr. Padfield used to come out from Exeter about once a month and he had a Bungalow opposite the Warren House Inn. There were some of the Warnes from Post Bridge working on the mine. I remember a big Waterwheel working on the mine and also a shaft on the Warren House Inn side of the mine known as Lanes shaft which my father started to clean up but he did not get very far with it. My father used to say it was good quality ferney tin which I think he meant it was the outcrop of a load. At that time the tin used to be sold at Tabbs Hotel Redruth in what was knowen as the Tin Ticketing and the Birch Tor Tin always fetched the top price. I remember my father very pleased once when Birch Tor sample made £130 a ton. When my father finished at Birch Tor he started at South Crofty as a Timberman when they started to sink New Cooks Shaft in fact he put the first set of Timber in New Cooks Shaft. He was at South Crofty 27 years.[15]

As at Golden Dagger Mine, underground work appears to have come to an end more or less at the outbreak of the First World War, though some surface work continued into the early 1920s.

During the First World War Philip Crosby Pope, a consulting engineer, became manager of surface work at Vitifer. His daughter, then a teenager, recalled how it happened:

Our father's health was not too good, & the doctor said he should have an open air life for a while . . . He came in contact with a man who wanted to form a Company to do some open-cast work at an old defunct tin mine on the moor (Dartmoor) . . . My father became Manager, and they had modern equipment. This, however, did not last very long because the process was not viable . . . the whole thing was above ground, and my sister and I remember the tin being 'panned'. Our family lived in a bungalow right on the mine, with only a cart-track leading to it . . . I know there was a stream there & arc lamps for working after dark. I remember it was hoped this work would help the war effort & the disappointment when it did not turn out to produce enough tin . . . A very foolish lady living in the area had 'spy mania' & reported activity going on at the mine after dark!! She reported my father to the Police as a suspected spy! . . . I remember the Police coming by car to the mine one day, and my father was, of course, able to satisfy them completely. But these things stick & it was quite a long time before the rumours died down!! . . . The bungalow was a wooden one, most of the rooms opening one out of the other, with just match-boarding separating them! The cooking was by Perfection Oil Cooker![16]

A joint lease for Birch Tor & Vitifer, Golden Dagger and lands adjoining was granted by the Duchy of Cornwall to Dartmoor Tin Mines Limited for twenty-one years from 1 March 1923. Dues were set at '1/24 on minerals worked from Dumps and alluvial and semi-alluvial minerals' and '1/40 on minerals raised from lodes underground', but it is believed that no underground work was actually done under this lease. Dues were also to be paid on 'granite and stone' at the rate of 3d per ton.[17]

From 1925 no active work was carried out at Vitifer although men employed at Golden Dagger lived in the bunkhouse there. The last known lease for working tin at Birch Tor & Vitifer was granted to Geoffrey N. T. Taylor for one year from 24 June 1938 with dues set at 1/30 and a rent of £20.[18] It is possible that some tin was removed from waste heaps under this grant. During the Second World War unexploded bombs were brought from Plymouth to be detonated at Vitifer and much disturbance was caused to surface remains, especially in the vicinity of the dressing-floors (see plates 26 and 36).

Notes and References to Birch Tor & Vitifer Tin Mine

1 Copy conveyance in R. Burnard's Ordnance Map of Dartmoor, Vol. 2, in possession of Lady S. Sayer
2 DuCo London/Dartmore Proceedings *passim*
3 Devon Record Office/564/Swete Vol. 15, 177–8
4 *Idem*/Vol. 16, pp.1–2
5 Cornwall Record Office/DDRG1/128–141
6 DuCo London/Bundle: Miscellaneous 1830–1835/16 Sept. 1834
7 *Idem*/3 Feb. 1835
8 DuCo London/Bundle: Miscellaneous 1836–1840/24 Oct. 1837
9 British Sessional Papers, House of Commons 1864, Vol. 24, Pt 2, Kinnaird Commission, pp. 449–452
10 DuCo Bradninch/Letters Sent/31 Jan. 1857, 26 June 1857, 17 Dec. 1858
11 *Idem*/16 June 1863
12 *Idem*/Letters Received/20 Jan. 1882
13 DuCo London/Mineral Grants Vol. 1; DuCo Bradninch/Letters Received/26 March 1888
14 DuCo London/Mineral Grants Vol. 1
15 G. Thomas *in litt.*, 29 April 1974; oral inf., 20 May 1974
16 Miss J. Pope *in litt.*, 19 Oct. 1976 and 3 Nov. 1976
17 DuCo London/Mineral Grants Vol. 1
18 *Idem*

Plate 20 *Old tin workings, Vitifer Mine, Postbridge, 1913*
Photographer: Chapman & Sons (no. 11956)
Grid reference: SX 68158087 (viewpoint)
Original loaned by R. Bellamy

This view is looking west-south-west along the Old Vitifer Lode. Note the human figure in the foreground. The opencast workings seen here are medieval in origin but had deep shafts sunk in the bottom in the eighteenth and nineteenth centuries. Dunstans Shaft is on the right, and was 40 fathoms (240 ft/73 m) deep (Broughton 1968/9).

Moses Bawden, a highly respected mine manager, wrote to a local newspaper in about 1903 concerning Birch Tor & Vitifer tin mines as follows:

From my first association with the management of these mines in 1864 I was particularly impressed with the enormous workings that must have been for centuries carried on to excavate such gullies as those at these mines. Tens of millions of tons of stuff must have been taken out of them to get down to water level. I know of no such evidence of ancient mining in any part of Devon and Cornwall as is seen here.[1]

Plate 21 *View northwards up the Redwater valley to the buildings of Vitifer Mine, c.1912*
Photographer: Chapman & Sons (no. 11952)
Grid reference: SX 682810 (buildings)
Original loaned by Mrs Nellie White

This mine complex is on open moorland at a height of 1200 ft (366 m) above sea-level. Little more than bare foundations now survives on site and this photograph illustrates well the appearance of a remote moorland mining settlement when active. The slope of Birch Tor is on the right. The track winding down the valley leads towards Golden Dagger Mine.

The building on the extreme left is the carpenter's shop. Further to the left, out of sight, were the blacksmith's shop and Dry. The large two-storey building next on the right was the 'Miners' House' where men would stay for the week in dormitories, having walked from villages on the edge of the moor.[2] The upper floor had a central corridor and was divided into cubicles. The ground floor contained a kitchen range and 'a sort of canteen'.[3] Mrs Nellie White (b. 1896) recalled parties or concerts being held there once or twice a year.[4] The building

appears to have been constructed in the early years of the century.

To the right of the Miners' House is a substantial stone building with a thatched roof very much like a typical Dartmoor farmhouse. This is clearly the oldest building on the site and very probably dates from the late eighteenth century. It was the mine captain's house and was occupied by Captain Richard and Anna Jory in the closing years of the nineteenth century and early this century. It had four bedrooms upstairs, and three downstairs rooms – kitchen, sitting-room and scullery/pantry/larder. It had no bathroom, and the toilet was in the garden, of which the produce included potatoes, cabbages and gooseberries. Anna Jory told her granddaughter, Elsie Coaker, that at the time of the Great Blizzard of March 1891 it was possible to walk out of the bedroom windows on to the snow, and that there were still patches of snow left in June. The Jorys always kept a bag of flour and a sack of potatoes handy for emergencies, and would salt down a pig for the winter.

Attached to the captain's house is another cottage where a mining family lived. Next on the right, the building with the prominent porch was the mine office, where accounts would be kept and the men paid their wages. It was also a home for John James Coaker and his family for about ten years between 1896 and 1906. Elsie Bellamy (née Coaker) was born above the office in 1896. As a young girl she had to collect milk from Headland Warren Farm, more than half a mile distant. Mrs Hannaford, the farmer's wife, sometimes gave her bread and cream to eat. A butcher called Hill delivered weekly to the mine from Chagford, as did a baker from Poundsgate called Withycombe. Elsie Bellamy remembered well his 4 lb loaves and that he often got tipsy in the Warren House Inn with the result that loaves were not infrequently found in the stream after minor accidents with his horse and cart.[5] Charles Hill of Chagford started delivering bread to Vitifer in 1916 and he remembers that he charged 5d for a 4 lb loaf. At this time, another baker, Owen Harvey of Widecombe, also delivered bread.[6]

To the right of the office is a bungalow, lived in by miners and their families. On the extreme right of the picture and detached from the other structures is an imposing bungalow with a veranda of wood and glass. This was built for the mine manager, Mr W. A. Padfield, but was burnt down, probably before the First World War.[7]

Plate 22 *View of Vitifer Mine from the south-west, c.1912*
Photographer: Chapman & Sons (no. 11955)
Grid reference: SX 682810
Copy provided by A. Robin Hood, 1985

This shows most of the buildings seen in plate 21, but from a different viewpoint, looking towards Birch Tor in the background.

Plate 23 *Working underground at Vitifer Mine, c.1912*
Photograph: Chapman & Sons (?)
Copy provided by Gilbert Warne

This photograph shows clearly the method of hand-drilling hard rock, a technique that had remained virtually unchanged for centuries. The men work in pairs, one holding the drill against the rock face and the other hammering it. Three of the men have taken off their hard hats, exposing the flannel skull-caps underneath. The other man has a candle stuck in his hat, and the two patches of brightness on the left of the picture are also likely to be candles, fixed to the rock face with lumps of clay. Miss Annie Leaman (b. 1894), whose brother Herbert worked for nine years as an underground miner at Vitifer in the early years of this century, was taken underground by him. She described conditions as very wet and 'rugged', and told how candles used to go out in bad air. Jack Hamlyn (b. 1883) also went underground and remembers well places where water was 'streaming down'.[8]

The two men on the upper level have not yet been identified with certainty, but bottom left is Freddy Warne and bottom right is John (Jack) Webb, both of Postbridge.

Freddy Warne was born in about 1877, the son of Solomon Warne, a tin miner. All except one of his six brothers were also miners (see figure 4 and plate 28). In the late 1920s he became Donald Smith's right-hand man at Golden Dagger Mine (see plates 43–69). In 1970 his nephew, Fernley Warne, produced a cutting from a magazine which recorded the following information about his uncle:

The last of the Dartmoor tin miners has left the Moor. Mr. Fred Warne of Postbridge spent 81 years working in and around the Dartmoor Mines . . . He left school when he was 13 and went straight to work. At that time he had to put in a 9-hour working shift either blasting or boring underground, after walking 4 or 5 miles to the mines. 'Some of the mines were very wet like Golden Dagger.

Others like Hexworthy were very dry', he recalled. 'Often we worked up to our middles in water but we just didn't bother about it in those days. I kept on working until I was 75 and then I thought it was time to slow down a bit.' In Mr. Warne's day the tin ore was sent to Redruth for smelting and processing, and Dartmoor tin was of the highest quality. 'The mines began to close down in 1920', he said. 'More than 20 or 30 miners went off to serve with the Sappers, but only a few of us came back. There were better livings to be made away from Dartmoor'. Soon the deep mines began to close, and a half hearted attempt was made at surface mining, but the yield was uneconomical . . . Although working in poor conditions, the Dartmoor miners had no welfare service organised for them. There was not even a hot meal available for them at the top of the shaft.[9]

John Webb was the son of Tom Webb, another Postbridge miner (see figure 4). His grandson, also called Tom Webb, still lives in Postbridge. John Webb was one of several Postbridge miners to be killed in the First World War, but several people remembered him for his lovely tenor voice and his singing in the chapel at Postbridge. At Christmas time he used to come out from underground singing carols.[10]

Plate 24 *Underground at Vitifer & Birch Tor Tin Mine, c.1912*
Photographer: Chapman & Sons (no. 11944)
Original given to Author by Miss Annie Leaman, 1974

Illustrated well here are the cramped conditions sometimes met underground on Dartmoor mines. The lower figure is standing on a sollar or stull, i.e. a wooden platform.[11] He is Sidney French, son of John French of Middle Merripit, Postbridge, and was born on 10 May 1889. He died on 9 May 1976. The man top left may be George Leaman and top right may be Dick French.[12]

Sidney French came from a farming family and had eight brothers and sisters, one of whom died in infancy. Two of his brothers also went mining. He began work at Vitifer Mine on 3 February 1903 and earned 1/9d a day as a buddle boy on the surface (see plate 26). He first worked underground at the age of about seventeen and eventually earned 24 shillings a week, which was considered good pay. Altogether he worked for ten years on Dartmoor tin mines – at Vitifer, Golden Dagger and Hexworthy. His first wife, Hilda, was the daughter of Captain Richard Jory of Vitifer Mine, and his second, Alberta, was the sister of Captain John James Coaker of Golden Dagger.

While working at Vitifer and Golden Dagger Sidney French lived at Middle Merripit, and recalled that breakfast before walking the two or three miles to the mine and starting a day's work consisted of 'a cup of tea and a piece of bread and cream'. Sometimes he had 'kittle broth', which was bread in a basin with hot water or tea poured over it and with a lump of butter added. Sometimes too he would have a piece of cake.

Picks, hammers and drills were provided by the mine. The underground shifts were 'forenoon' (7 a.m.–3 p.m.), 'afternoon' (3 p.m.–11 p.m.) and 'night' (11 p.m.–7 a.m.). Miners would work five shifts in a week unless they were on forenoon shift, in which case they would do a sixth shift on Saturday morning but would leave work at 1 p.m. The forenoon shift workers would have a half-hour break from 10.00 to 10.30 for 'crib', i.e. pasties or sandwiches. If employed on the surface men would work from 7 a.m. to 5 p.m. and would be allowed a half-hour break from 9.30 to 10.00 and an hour for lunch from 1.00 to 2.00 (1.00–1.30 in winter). There were no holidays except bank holidays, for which the men received no pay. Sidney French remembered being paid fortnightly and having to put sixpence aside for the doctor in case of illness or injury.

Of conditions underground he recalled:

Of course in some places, 'twould be very bad working, you know. You'd [be] in an end, working in an end, you'd blast two or three or three or four holes, and you'd have the dynamite smoke. Well, they'd blast, say, half past two, and you'd go in three o'clock. Well, the place 'twould be all full of smoke sometimes, you see. That was bad. But of course, sometimes where you was up, stoping up, 'twould be more air like – the smoke would go, you see. But in an end it would be bad sometimes, yes.

In summer, men like Sidney French would often help on farms in the evenings after a day's work underground. Sidney French recalled leaving work from a forenoon shift at two or three o'clock and going to help at Runnage Farm:

Us went back every night, every afternoon of the week. Cor, Saturday I was . . . Saving hay for ten, half past ten. Then you'd go in, have supper and then you had to walk home from Runnage to [Middle] Merripit then out again half past five, quarter to six. Oh, I was runned up.

After leaving Vitifer Mine in 1913, Sidney French got a contract from the Council for the road between Two Bridges and the Warren Inn, breaking and rolling stones. From 1916 to 1919 he was in the army in India and Mesopotamia. He then came home and took on his father's farm of Middle Merripit. 'There I stopped,' he told me.

Claude Warne (b. 1901) lived at Middle Merripit when a young boy and remembers seeing Sidney French, his brother Dick French, and Silas Sleep set off to the mines to work and return home dirty. They would clean themselves in a stream with a bucket of water, which would turn into a bucket of mud.[13]

Plate 25 *Water-wheel and dressing-floors at Vitifer Mine from the south-east, c.1915*
Photographer: Unknown   *Grid reference:* SX 68328071
Original loaned by Mrs Brook and Miss Mortimore, 1974

The upper part of the large stamps water-wheel can just be seen over the top of the sheds in the foreground. Note the ladder propped against the launder bringing water to the wheel. The pale heap in front of the launder carried a tramway direct to the stamps from the main Vitifer adit level, which was driven eastwards into the side of the hill towards Headland.

The sheds housed the stamps and dressing-floor for the mine (see plates 26 and 27). The chimney on

the left was connected with a process for drying the tin concentrate. The small water-wheel to the left of the chimney may have powered a round buddle or possibly a mechanical kieve (see plates 26 and 27).

The wheel and floors date from 1902/3 as Sidney French recalled that, when he started work here in February 1903, a new wheelpit was being made and the wheel installed.[14]

In the background, through the launder, can be seen the main mine buildings of Vitifer, especially the Miners' House (cf. plates 21 and 22). The left-hand building with the small chimney was the Dry.

Plate 26 *Round buddles, dressing-floor and view
northwards to Vitifer Mine buildings, c.1912*
Photographer: Chapman & Sons (no. 11950)
Grid reference: SX 68328071
Reproduced from Smith (1983, p.48), with permission

The large water-wheel seen here is the one in plate 25. Three men are digging tin concentrate from a round buddle and there is another buddle behind them. (For a description of the technique see plate 42.) Plate 36 shows one of these buddles in its ruined state. The buildings in the background are those shown more clearly in plates 21 and 22.

This photograph is a recent discovery and it has not been possible to identify any of the men. However, Frank Warne (b. 1901), the son of Captain William Warne of Vitifer, started work as a buddle boy here at the age of thirteen. He and other boys had to report for work at 7 a.m. but would sometimes be given 'task work' which involved cleaning out a certain number of buddles. Frank Warne commented, 'So we were fond of fishing and shooting. We used to get in with the barrows, and we'd have 'em out by dinner time.' They would then be free for the rest of the day.[15]

Plate 27 *The dressing-floor, Vitifer Mine, c.1905*
Photographer: Chapman & Sons (no. 11949)
Grid reference: SX 68328071
Original given to Author by Mrs Page, 1976

This is a view of the interior of the sheds in plate 25. Several piles of tin concentrate can be seen in the centre of the picture. This is the consistency the tin would have after being crushed by the stamps and passed through the round buddles. In the foreground are two large wooden tubs and one smaller one. These are kieves or 'chimming kieves'. Donald Smith, who learnt the techniques of tin dressing at Golden Dagger Mine, twenty years after this photograph was

taken, described the kieving process as follows:

A kieve was half filled with water and the water stirred by a rotary action with a special shovel in the hands of one man, while the heads (concentrates) were introduced a little at a time by another worker, until anything up to 3 cwt was in suspension in the water. This is very hard work when the water becomes like thin mud. When the tin dresser judges the time is right, the stirring stops and the side of the kieve is tapped to help the particles to settle in the kieve and pack down hard. The heavier tin will settle first and when the water is poured out the kieve, now on its side, would be in a good position for the

dresser to scrape the top surface away for 'tailings' and the next inch or two for 'middles', and the bottom section as 'heads' which is judged for quality by vanning a little sample and noting the width of the tin band. Chimming kieves varied slightly in size, the smaller being used for the final chimming before bagging.[16]

In this picture the boy in the foreground is probably doing the initial stirring, while the man behind him has his arm resting on an upturned kieve in the position it would be in when the concentrate was ready to be scraped from it. The small kieve has a vanning shovel laid across it. Of particular interest is the contraption against the side of the shed behind the kieves. This includes a chimming paddle for use instead of a man stirring with a shovel and also part of a mechanical 'packer'. The packer was worked by a water-wheel whereby the kieve was slightly tilted on edge (part of one can just be seen behind the moustachioed man) and hit by an 'arm' with tappets on it. Frank Warne recalled this machine in use and remembered that Will Lentern the blacksmith made all the ironwork for it.[17]

Next to the white-bearded man in the centre is a 'square buddle'. This was essentially a rectangular trough in which tin concentrate mixed with water was spread and then settled out, as if it was a section across a round buddle. A short plank can be seen resting against a wooden box (?). This would have been laid across the buddle and the tin dresser would have sat on it while agitating the concentrate with a heather brush (which can also be seen on the box) in order to create riffles for the good-quality tin to catch against. Running along the edge of the shed are wooden launders bringing water for the processes.

Note also the electric light bulbs, complete with lampshades. Vitifer Mine had its own turbine generating electricity. When Frank Warne worked here they used discarded bulbs as barometers. The old-fashioned bulbs had projecting 'nibs' and Frank Warne remembered:

And if we had one fused, we used to knock the nib off, full 'im with water and 'ang 'im up ... If it was going to be wet he'd start to drip. If it was going to dry weather with the dry air he'd keep the water in.[18]

There are seven men in the photograph, three of whom have been positively identified. The lad in the foreground is Sidney French (see plate 24),[19] and next to him on the right, with the bushy moustache, is Thomas (Tommy) Webb of Postbridge. He was born in 1865,[20] the son of Thomas Webb, a tin miner. He was first employed in the Postbridge mines at the age of nine. It is said that his mother and father never knew where the next meal was coming from. It may well be that this uncertainty led Tommy Webb to acquire great skill in snaring rabbits, for which he is still remembered.[21] He was crippled by arthritis in old age, yet was ninety-two years and nine months old when he died in October 1957. His home was at Stannon Lodge.[22]

The man in the centre with the white beard is Captain Richard Jory. He was known as 'Captain Dick'. Born in Cornwall in about 1846, he was a mining man all his life. He came from Newlyn to Postbridge in the 1870s, to work at Vitifer Mine under the management of Moses Bawden. He married a Miss Anna Maria Bickell of Postbridge. In retirement he and his wife lived at 'Cape Horn' (plate 31), and he died on 30 December 1915, aged sixty-nine. He was responsible for the everyday working of both Vitifer and Golden Dagger Mine, and kept all the mine accounts. His two sons, Harold and William, were both miners and four of his five daughters married miners, including John James Coaker, who was to be captain of Golden Dagger, and Jack Warne, who became captain of Hexworthy Mine (see figure 4).[23]

The man holding the wheelbarrow on the extreme left of the photograph may be Jim Webb.[24]

Most of the equipment illustrated here is very traditional and would not have been unfamiliar to the Dartmoor tinner of the sixteenth century.

Plate 28 *Tin miners outside the Dry (?), Vitifer Mine, c.1912*
Photographer: Chapman & Sons (no. 11947)
Grid reference: SX 68188097
Original given to Author by Miss Annie Leaman, 1974

The building behind the men has not been identified for certain but it is thought to be the Dry where the men could change and dry their underground clothes.

From left to right the men are the following:

1. Harry Warne (1877–1941). The son of Solomon Warne, a miner, he started mining at the age of nine

and died at Vitifer aged sixty-four. He was widely known as 'Silvertop'. His daughter, Mrs Brook of Postbridge, heard it said that his generation was brought up on bread and brown sugar – he was one of seven brothers and two sisters.[25] See also plates 29 and 68.

2. John Sowden. He is remembered as an old man working at both Golden Dagger Mine and Vitifer Mine. Reginald Warne (b. 1898), who was brought up at Middle Merripit, recalls that he was known as 'Captain' Sowden and clearly remembers seeing him

35

making his way to the chapel in Postbridge. He was a regular chapel man.[26] For a time he lived at Pizwell.[27] See also plate 29.

3. Unknown

4. Freddy Warne. A brother of Harry and William (no.6), his life was spent in mining. See plate 23.

5. Unknown

6. William Warne. A brother of Harry and Freddy, he is thought to have taken over from Captain John Webb as captain of Vitifer Mine.[28] The fact that his clothing in this photograph is different to that of the other men suggests that he was captain when it was taken. His home was Lydgate, Postbridge.[29] His wife was a sister of Jim Webb, the tin dresser, of Postbridge. William was killed in 1921 in an accident involving a horse and cart on the road to Dartmeet.[30]

7. William Herbert (Bert) White. A Postbridge man, it is remembered that he worked underground with Lewis Evely (no.8).[31] He married Ethel, the daughter of Captain Richard Jory of Vitifer, and his sister married Ethel's brother William. He too was tragically killed. Fernley Warne (b. 1907, son of George Warne of Middle Merripit) told me that Bert White was travelling on a cart with his father where there is 'a little bit of a pinch', i.e. rising ground, as you go from Statts Brook Bridge towards Postbridge. He had apparently got down from the cart to pick something off the road when he was struck by a car.[32]

8. Lewis Evely (born *c.* 1884). This man is an interesting example of a miner from the north side of Dartmoor who found employment in the Postbridge mines. He was one of fifteen or sixteen children and was brought up at Hullacombe Ford, Whiddon Down (SX 691934). His brother, Fred Evely of Bow, remembers him leaving home at 4 a.m. on Monday mornings, setting out for Vitifer Mine, nearly eight miles distant as the crow flies, and taking food with him for the week, including tins of condensed milk,

bacon and butter. He returned on Saturdays.[33] When he was courting his future wife, Marina Hill of Shilstone Farm, Throwleigh, he sometimes lodged there. His future brother-in-law, Tom Hill, remembered that he sometimes left the farm for Vitifer two hours early 'to trim the lamps'. These were apparently oil-lamps in the miners' cubicles in the Miners' House.[34] He was married in 1910 and for twelve months the couple lived at Shilstone (SX 660901), still more than six miles in a direct line to Vitifer. Mrs Polly Osborn (née Hill) and Mrs Agnes Evely (née Hill), his sisters-in-law, remember him cycling to Vitifer from Shilstone, taking a reed basket with a lid in which would be bread, bacon, pasties, tea, sugar, etc., for his week's supplies. Lewis then moved back to Whiddon Down with his wife, to a cottage at Hobhouse (SX 698921).[35] He was also a local preacher and appears in a photograph of church leaders taken in 1906 (Court 1927, plate facing p. 104 – he is on the extreme right of the back row). In 1914 he and his wife emigrated to North America and were in mid-Atlantic when the First World War broke out.[36]

There were many other men who travelled from the South Zeal area to work at the Postbridge mines. When Ramsley Mine closed in 1909, Aubrey Tucker from Sticklepath was one of these. He used to travel across the moor with a friend. They had one pony between them so they adopted the 'ride and tied' method, whereby one rode ahead and the other walked. After a certain distance the one riding tethered the pony and started walking, enabling the other to reach the pony, catch up and overtake, and so repeat the process.[37]

Both Bert White and Lewis Evely are wearing leather gaiters known locally as 'skiddy-bags'.[38] Some of the other men are wearing 'Yorks' – pieces of string or leather straps tied below the knee to keep the bottom of the trouser leg out of the worst of the mud and to give looseness to the trouser knee. Also visible on the right of the photograph are some dynamite boxes.

Plate 29 *Tin miners outside the Warren House Inn (?),*
          c.1910
Photographer: Unknown
Original loaned by Miss Mortimore, 1974

These men have been photographed on a good road surface, which makes the only likely location to be at or near the Warren House Inn. Yet it is strange that they should be photographed there in their mining clothes, and also the details of the building behind them do not tally with the elevation of the Warren Inn against the road as seen in plate 30.

Three of the men are also in plate 28. Identifications are the following:

Standing from left to right
1. Harry Warne (see plate 28)
2. Unknown
3. Frank Rensfield (?) – compare plate 39
4. John Sowden (see plate 28)

Kneeling from left to right
1. Harry Westcott
2. Unknown
3. Lewis Evely (see plate 28)

Harry Westcott is of special interest. Born in 1861 in North Molton, he married a girl from Chudleigh. He was a cobbler and harness-maker by trade and eventually settled at Rixhill near Tavistock (SX 479723). For some reason, from about 1900 onwards he found employment as a miner. He nearly drowned in Anderton Mine near Rixhill.[39]

Amazingly, Vitifer Mine attracted men from even the far west of the moor. With several companions, including Fred Bayle, William Friend and a man called Toys, Harry Westcott travelled weekly to Vitifer before the First World War, a distance of nearly fourteen miles as the crow flies.[40] Frank Hodge, who farmed at Lower Tor, Rixhill, knew him well and remembered him walking to Vitifer before 1907:

They used to go through Whitchurch, across Whitchurch Down golf course, up over Vixen Tor, then come out on the road just above Merrivale pub, Tavistock side, then walk on again over the bridge and take the short cut up to the old school, Mission Hall School. Well, then they had to take road all the way from there on, right on all the way, from Rundlestone right to Two Bridges and on, and carry their food with them. Then they used to come home again for a change of clothing and food again Friday nights. Go away Sundays and come home Friday. They missed Saturday's work. They didn't used to work in the mine on the Saturday, you see. They poor devils used to do all that walking, then they got fed up with walking and got a bit older and got a pony and trap.[41]

Sidney French worked with him and remembered him as 'a nice fella'. He remembered too that he brought a son with him, also called Harry and aged about fourteen or fifteen.[42] This boy died in India during the First World War.[43] Sidney recalled that their pony was kept for them during their working week. Harry Westcott senior was blind in one eye.[44]

Plate 30   *The Warren House Inn, 1912*
Photographer: Chapman & Sons (no.11742)
Grid reference: SX 67428094
Negative in possession of Devon Record Office, reproduced with permission

This lonely public house, 1425 ft (434 m) above sea-level, was much frequented by tin miners when this photograph was taken. The publican was Tommy Hext, and Frank Hodge (b. 1887) described the pub as follows:

Old man Hext had that, and he had a big beard right down to here, and he stood about six foot two. Well, you'd go in the passageway like that, like you do now, then turn in to the left, and there was a big bare room, there wasn't a picture or anything in it, and you sot in the window, a great long seat like this in the long window and a long form [i.e. bench] ... [There] was two oil-lamps and over there was the peat fire. That fire was always in, always in. Used to be a chute thing hanging down like a funnel with no hole at the bottom, like a funnel shape with a long handle, and the men used to stand that one in the peat fire and get it hot and pour their quart of ale in it, get it hot, when you see it was hot, come and put in their quarts or their pints and drink it. Well, the old man used to draw all his ale from out in the back yard.[45]

Sidney French (b. 1889), a tin miner, recalled that beer was 2½d a pint and an ounce of tobacco 3½d when Mr Hext was there.[46] Jim Endacott (b. 1889) said Tommy Hext was always stroking his beard, and that Mrs Hext would shuffle along to take your order then disappear out the back.[47]

Some miners lodged for the week in the Warren House. Many miners who walked weekly to and fro from South Zeal to the mines would stop for refreshment here. Frank Webber (b. 1890) of East Week, Throwleigh, was told that miners walking from South Zeal once stopped for a drink before starting work and that it snowed so heavily that they were obliged to remain the rest of the day there![48]

Plate 31 *West Bungalow, c.1912, with view to the south-east and Soussons Down*
Photographer: Chapman & Sons (no.11726)
Grid reference: SX 67228070
Original given to Author by Mrs Winnie Murch, 1977

This bungalow was on the south side of the road between the Warren House Inn and Postbridge. It was in a very exposed position, 1425 ft (434 m) above sea-level, and was known locally as 'Cape Horn'. It was in fact typical of buildings put up on moorland mines at the turn of the century (cf. plate 32).

Several mining families occupied it at various times, including Captain Richard Jory and his wife Anna in their retirement.[49] Another miner who lived here for a time was Frank Hellier (1872–1935), who worked at both Vitifer Mine and Golden Dagger Mine and who married Helen, the sister of Captain John James Coaker. He also worked at Ramsley Mine, South Zeal, living at Mill Cottages, Sticklepath.[50]

Only the barest foundations can be seen on the site now.

Plate 32 *King's Oven Bungalow, Warren House Inn, 1 May 1976*
Photographer: Author   *Grid reference:* SX 67538107

Similar to West Bungalow (plate 31) in style, this building lay on the north side of the road between the Warren House Inn and Bush Down. It was built by Moses Bawden, manager of Vitifer Mine and Golden Dagger Mine, in the late nineteenth century and was locally known as 'Bawden's Bungalow'. Moses Bawden was one of the best-known mining personalities in Devon in the second half of the nineteenth century. He had been associated with Birch Tor & Vitifer Mine since 1864 (see plate 20) and had also managed Whiteworks Mine, besides being connected with Wheal Crebor near Tavistock and Devon Great Consols in the Tamar valley, being secretary of the latter (Burt *et al.* 1984, p.42). In the opinion of Mrs Nellie White of Postbridge he 'brought more work to Postbridge than anybody else that I know in those days',[51] a view shared by local mining historian Derek Broughton, who felt that he 'perhaps did more for Dartmoor mining than any other person' (Broughton 1971, p.13).

Moses Bawden stayed in the bungalow when visiting the mine monthly from Tavistock.[52] One of his daughters, who was consumptive, also stayed there. Mrs Elsie Bellamy (b. 1896) remembered him visiting Vitifer Mine on a pony which he would keep in a stable at the back of the bungalow. He had a fine upright bearing, 'a beautiful white beard' and was, in

Elsie Bellamy's words, 'a dear old gent'. He was sometimes accompanied on his visits by several other men and Anna Jory would cook them all a large lunch.[53] Ethel White (b. 1882), the daughter of Richard and Anna Jory, also recalled these visits. She well remembered her mother cooking a leg of mutton for Moses Bawden and that she and her siblings would be given the leftovers. In her opinion, he was 'a 'ansom man'.[54]

Regrettably, this historic link with Dartmoor's mining past was demolished as an 'eyesore' in 1976.

Plate 33 *Miss Gertrude Chudley outside Vitifer Mine buildings, c.1907*
Photographer: Unknown   *Grid reference:* SX 68248101
Original loaned by Mrs G. Prew

Gertrude Chudley was born at Gobbett near Hexworthy in 1892 (see plate 16). She was one of a family of twelve children and her father was James Chudley, who was employed at Hexworthy Mine (see plate 17).

At the age of about fifteen she spent a few months at Vitifer Mine, looking after a child of the Slade family, whom she is holding in this photograph.[55] Mrs Slade was employed as caretaker for the Miners' House.[56] Gertrude Chudley also looked after Arthur Willcocks, the mongol son of the 'Chief Agent' of the mine (Burt *et al.* 1984, p.16). She remembered that one of her great pleasures at the time was to wash her hair then climb to the top of Birch Tor and sit on a rock to dry it.[57]

One day when returning to the mine from church at Postbridge, she saw something by the side of the road which she thought was a large dog, but when she got closer she saw it was a man, who started to chase her. However, she managed to outrun him and reached the mine safely. That evening, the brother of Captain Bennetts of Vitifer was walking in the same area when he sensed someone behind him. He turned and saw a man about to hit him with a piece of wood. He gave chase but the man got away. A few days later the same man called at the Warren House Inn and drank a pint of beer belonging to Harry 'Silvertop' Warne. Although small, Harry Warne challenged the stranger. He and his fellow miners then grabbed him, took him outside the pub down to the mine leat on the other side of the road, threw him in and washed him up and down several times. His hat was thrown after him, and it is said that he was never seen again in the area.[58]

Plate 34 *Abandoned stamps water-wheel at Vitifer Mine, c.1930, viewed from the north-west*
Photographer: Unknown   *Grid reference:* SX 68338072
Original loaned by Mrs D. Hannaford, 1976

This is the same wheel as that seen in plates 25 and 26. Something of its size can be gauged by the figure on the right, who is the sister of Mrs Deborah Hannaford.[59] On the extreme right can be seen the small chimney-stack also visible in plates 25 and 36.

Plate 35 *Abandoned stamps water-wheel at Vitifer Mine, c.1935*
Photographer: Unknown   *Grid reference:* SX 68338072
Copy provided by W. Dodd, 1978

The man on the wheel is Mr W. Dodd, who was born in Chagford in 1912. Vitifer Mine was a favourite place for him to pick whortleberries. He and others remember that the cast-iron frame of the wheel had the maker's name on it – PEARCE of TAVISTOCK.[60] Note the stonework of the leat embankment in the background.

Plate 36 *The site of Vitifer Mine dressing-floors, 28 August 1937*
Photographer: P.H.G. Richardson *Grid reference:* SX 68328071

Compare this photograph with plate 26. The remains of a round buddle are in the foreground. Note also the chimney-stack and compare with plates 25 and 34. The ruins of some of the mine buildings can be seen on the left of the picture.

Virtually nothing is visible at this site today apart from the position of the buddle. Most of the remaining features were destroyed during the Second World War when unexploded bombs were brought from Plymouth to be detonated here.[61]

Plate 37 *Vitifer Mine: general view looking north-eastwards to Birch Tor, c.1950*
Photographer: Unknown   *Grid reference:* SX 682810
Original loaned by Mrs D. Hannaford, 1976

In the foreground can be seen the chimney-stack attached to the Dry at Vitifer Mine. This is the one that is just visible in the background of plate 25. It has since been razed to the ground.

On the right are the substantial ruins of the carpenter's shop, and in the centre of the picture is the site of the Miners' House, mine captain's house, etc. A similar view was taken by Eric Hemery in 1954 (Hemery 1983, p.618, plate 307). Little is visible here now besides some walling of the carpenter's shop.

Notes and References to Plates 20–37

1 Letter to local newspaper, 21 Jan. 1903 (?), on back of sheet 99SE in Vol.1 of R. Burnard's 6in. Ordnance Map of Dartmoor, in possession of Lady S. Sayer

2 Oral inf., Frank Warne, 30 Oct. 1973

3 Oral inf., Garfield Thomas, 20 May 1974 *et al.*

4 Oral inf., Mrs Nellie White, 21 June 1972 (tape)

5 Oral inf., Mrs Elsie Bellamy (née Coaker), 18 July 1976

6 Oral inf., Charles Hill, 4 Nov. 1977

7 Oral inf., Mrs Nellie White, 21 June 1972 (tape)

8 Oral inf., Miss Annie Leaman and John Hamlyn, 5 July 1973

9 Copied into Author's notebook, 11 Sept. 1970

10 Oral inf., Mrs Ethel White (née Jory), 30 Oct. 1973; Sidney French, 4 Feb. 1974

11 Oral inf., Frank Warne, 30 Oct. 1973 (tape)

12 Oral inf., Reginald Warne, 20 May 1975

13 Oral inf., Sidney French, 4 Feb. 1974 (tape) and 7 Nov. 1974; C. Warne, 19 July 1984

14 Oral inf., Sidney French, 4 Feb. 1974 (tape)

15 Oral inf., Frank Warne, 30 Oct. 1973 (tape)

16 D. Smith *in litt.*, 8 March 1978

17 Oral inf., Frank Warne, 30 Oct. 1973; D. Smith *in litt.*, 8 March 1978

18 Oral inf., Frank Warne, 30 Oct. 1973 (tape)

19 Oral inf., Sidney French, 4 Feb. 1974 (tape)

20 Oral inf., Mrs Eva Webb, 22 Feb. 1974

21 Oral inf., Mrs Emmie Webb, 8 April 1974

22 Oral inf., Mrs Eva Webb, 22 Feb. 1974; Tom Webb, 24 April 1975

23 Oral inf., Mrs Ethel White, 30 Oct. 1973; Mrs Elsie Bellamy, 18 July 1976; Mrs Winnie Murch (née Jory), 25 May 1977

24 Oral inf., Mrs Elsie Bellamy, 18 July 1976

25 Oral inf., Mrs Brook (née Warne), 26 Sept. 1973, etc.

26 Oral inf., Reginald Warne, 20 May 1975 (tape)

27 Oral inf., Miss Annie Sleep, 24 May 1974

28 Oral inf., Sidney French, 25 April 1974

29 Oral inf., Frank Warne, 30 Oct. 1973 (tape)

30 Oral inf., Mrs Bents, 30 Oct. 1973

31 Oral inf., Sidney French, 25 April 1974

32 Oral inf., Fernley Warne, 11 June 1984

33 Oral inf., Fred Evely, 13 Jan. 1979

34 Oral inf., Tom Hill, 29 Oct. 1978

35 Oral inf., Mrs Polly Osborn and Mrs Agnes Evely, 2 Aug. 1979

36 *Idem*

37 Oral inf., Mr and Mrs A. Wannacott, 17 Sept. 1969

38 Oral inf., Mrs Eva Webb, 22 Feb. 1974

39 Oral inf., I. Westcott, 29 March 1973 and 16 June 1976

40 Oral inf., Frank Hodge, 29 Dec. 1972 (tape); I. Westcott, 29 March 1973; Mrs Burley, 11 June 1973; Sidney French, 4 Feb. 1974 (tape)

41 Oral inf., Frank Hodge, 29 Dec. 1972 (tape)

42 Oral inf., Sidney French, 7 Nov. 1974

43 Oral inf., I. Westcott, 29 March 1973

44 Oral inf., Sidney French, 4 Feb. 1974 (tape)

45 Oral inf., Frank Hodge, 29 Dec. 1972 (tape)

46 Oral inf., Sidney French, 7 Nov. 1974

47 Oral inf., Jim Endacott, 6 Dec. 1973. The Hexts also provide a link between Dartmoor and the painter Augustus John, for in about 1905 his companion, Dorelia, gave birth to a boy in a caravan nearby, and was looked after by them.

48 Oral inf., Frank Webber, 7 May 1974

49 Oral inf., Mrs Elsie Bellamy, 18 July 1976

50 Oral inf., G. Hellier, 7 Dec. 1973

51 Oral inf., Mrs Nellie White, 21 June 1972 (tape)

52 Oral inf., Sidney French, 17 Dec. 1975

53 Oral inf., Mrs Elsie Bellamy, 18 July 1976

54 Oral inf., Mrs Ethel White, 30 Oct. 1973

55 Oral inf., Mrs G. Prew, 9 July 1977

56 Oral inf., Charles Hill, 4 Nov. 1977

57 Oral inf., Mrs G. Prew, 9 July 1977

58 *Idem* and 23 Oct. 1979 (tape)

59 Oral inf., Mrs Deborah Hannaford, 18 July 1976

60 Oral inf., W. Dodd, 7 Feb. 1978 and 23 Feb. 1978; Chris Hill, 19 Oct. 1983

61 Oral inf., G. Hambley, 29 Jan. 1974

Golden Dagger Tin Mine

An Outline History

This mine is situated about half a mile (800 m) south of Birch Tor & Vitifer, in the parish of Manaton (see figure 3, p.22). Its history is relatively poorly recorded, there being only brief accounts in the standard works on Dartmoor mining. Although the mine almost certainly has a medieval origin, the first mention of its very unusual name did not occur until the mid-nineteenth century. In October 1855 a sale advertisement appeared in the *Mining Journal* for 'One Half of the Interest granted by the sett of John P. Bastard Esq. in the promising tin mine called the Golden Dagger, situate near Post Bridge, on Dartmoor',[1] and in the same year it was recorded that a large stone of tin from the mine had been placed at the disposal of the Duchy of Cornwall for display at the 'Great Exhibition' in Paris.[2]

From another reference it appears that the mine had been working under the name of Golden Dagger since at least 1851 but that ore from it was sold privately and in the name of various persons.[3] It is also known that a tin stamping mill and a small cottage existed more or less on the site of Dinah's House (SX 685800) from at least the early nineteenth century, as 'Stamping Mills' are marked here on the one-inch-to-the-mile map published by the Ordnance Survey in 1809.[4] In about 1825 mention was made of 'the tinworks called the Stamps' at this locality.[5]

It is interesting that the name Golden Dagger was first recorded in the 1850s, some twenty years before the discovery in 1872 of a prehistoric dagger pommel of amber decorated with tiny gold pins in the northernmost barrow at Two Barrows on Hameldown only a mile and a half (2½ km) south-east of the mine (Grinsell 1978, p.156). It thus seems likely that a metal object, perhaps of bronze or decorated with gold, had been found in the immediate vicinity of the mine in the period between 1830 and 1850 which caused such a striking name to be given to it. It is possible that a barrow on Soussons Down was disturbed by miners or that something was found among streamworks in the valley bottom.

In 1879 Moses Bawden first became involved in the mine and held grants of the sett.[6] For nearly a quarter of a century he remained closely linked with the mine as secretary and chief agent and is said to have spent £20 000 there (Burt *et al.* 1984, p.66; Le Messurier 1966, p.83). From 1880 the mine appears in the official *Mineral Statistics* recording production, management and employment (Burt *et al.* 1984, pp.65–7). A peak was reached in 1892, when forty-one persons were employed and tin valued at £1530 was produced (Burt *et al.* 1984, p.66).

From 1880 to 1913 men were almost continuously employed on the mine. For part of this period the mine was worked in conjunction with Hexworthy Mine by Dartmoor Minerals Limited. Underground work was abandoned on 1 August 1914 (H.M.S.O. 1958), but after the First World War and in the 1920s surface work was carried on, exploiting the waste heaps left by earlier generations of tinners. One company was apparently called the Centrifugal Concrete Construction Company,[7] and another was

Dartmoor Tin Mines Limited, who went into liquidation in about 1923.[8] The last company to do any substantial work was Torr Trust Limited, which began work in February 1925 but was forced to close the mine on 12 November 1930 owing to the low price of tin.[9] It was during this last period of work that Donald Smith was employed first as electrical and mechanical engineer from Christmas 1925 and then as manager from 1927 onwards (see plates 43–69).

Small quantities of tin were extracted from the alluvial heaps in the 1930s and there was talk of getting the mine going on a proper basis once more (see plate 73). Philip B. S. Stanhope was granted leases by the Duchy of Cornwall of Golden Dagger Mine and an alluvial area to the south during 1938, but only until the end of the year, and no further work seems to have been done.[10]

Notes and References to Golden Dagger Tin Mine

1 *Mining Journal* 20 Oct. 1855, p.678
2 DuCo Bradninch/Letters Sent/20 Jan. 1855
3 DuCo Bradninch/Letters Sent/30 Nov. 1858; 10 Jan. 1859
4 Reprint published by David & Charles (Newton Abbot), 1969
5 Bodleian MS. Top. Devon d.1 fol. 104. See also DuCo London/Bundle: Miscellaneous 29 December 1834; Manaton Census Schedule 1851 re 'Stamp Cottage'
6 DuCo Bradninch/Letters Sent/26 March 1881; Letters Received/4 June 1888
7 Oral inf., H. Trude, 19 Sept. 1969
8 D. Smith *in litt.*, 5 Oct. 1970
9 Note in possession of Mrs Eva Webb, 22 Feb. 1974
10 DuCo London Mineral Grants Vol. 1

Plate 38   *Scene underground, Golden Dagger Tin Mine, c.1912*
Photographer: Chapman & Sons (no. 11941)[1]
Original loaned by R. Bellamy

This shows very clearly the wet and difficult conditions that existed in parts of the mine. The narrow vein of tin ore can be seen as a dark vertical streak in the centre of the picture. If photographs had existed in the late sixteenth century, a scene such as this might well have been used to illustrate the words of John Hooker, writing of the Dartmoor tinner in about 1590:

> *His lyffe most commonly is in pyttes and caves under the grounde of a greate depth and in great daunger because the earthe above his hedd is in sundry places crossed and posted over with tymber to keepe the same from fallinge* (Blake 1915, p.342).

Little had changed in three hundred years. Iron bars glisten in the wet, and a wooden pick handle can be seen resting against the lower strut.

William Withycombe (born *c.* 1891), local postman for thirty-nine years, recalled an accident at Golden Dagger Mine when for some reason men working on a stope were unaware that a fuse had been lit for blasting below them:

> *When they come down they just saw this yer fuse spitting you see, and they knew then what was on, you know. However, it did go off and some of 'em caught it, you know – splinters and that. They was off work for a bit, but nothing very serious, you know.*[2]

Annie Sleep (b. 1892) remembered a story told her by her father, Silas Sleep, about a fatality at Golden Dagger, and the manner of breaking the news to the miner's wife:

> *One day . . . one of the men was underground and he got killed and the woman that lived there, called Robins, used to live in one of them [buildings] called Dinah's House. And they said, 'Who was to go up and tell the poor old*

'Oh,' he said, 'you'll know it directly when the skip comes up.' And that's how he broke the sad news.[3]

The man in the foreground is George Coaker, brother to Captain 'John James'. He was known as 'Cape Horn' George.[4] The two men in the background are unidentified though the lower one is possibly Johnny Wills of Ashburton, who is second from the left in plate 39.

When Sidney French (1889–1976) first went to work underground at Golden Dagger, the men had to use the Dry at Vitifer, walking all the way up the valley in their wet clothes:

Some places it was wet, some places it was warm. And you'd come out from underground sometimes all wet and hot and before you could get up to the Dry – 'twas a long ways up from where us used to come out from the level – you'd take off your coat and he'd stand up, freezed through. It takes a bit of believing but is quite right . . . You'd be in there, you'd be hot, sweating and all that. When you come out . . . you'd be going right up against the wind.[5]

Despite this, Sidney French clearly found satisfaction from his work:

I used to like Dagger. Dagger Mine was a nice little mine to work in . . . We were up there working, up Dagger. Us didn't go in the level, us went up the gully and went down a little shaft, a little air shaft and 'twasn't very deep down and we had a lode there . . . and he was solid, he was solid with tin and us worked there, oh I don't know, for a brave old while. Me and me brother, us was one shift, and Freddy [Warne] and Jack Webb they was other shift, and Jimmy [Webb] – Uncle Jimmy – he was the boss there then to Dagger. Us used to go in for so long then us used to come out to the floors and clean up the tin. There wasn't very many of us there, just eight or nine of us, I think. Us was there for a brave bit like that. Then this yer lode he got runned out or he wasn't so good . . . But he was a lovely little lode for some time. Solid tin he was.[6]

lady that her husband had been killed?' And anyway, one old chap went up to tell her, and he went up and he said, 'Can you tell me please, do Widow Robins live here?' 'Widow Robins, indeed,' she said, 'I'm Mrs Robins.'

Plate 39 *Tin miners outside the adit level at Golden*
Dagger Mine, c.1912
Photographer: Chapman & Sons (no. 11937)
Grid reference: SX 68228037
Original given to Author by Mrs Page, 1976

This is one of the most evocative of all photographs of

Dartmoor tin miners. It also happens to be the first that I was shown (in August 1970 by Miss Annie Sleep), and caused me to search for others. Note the tools the men are holding, the candles stuck in lumps of clay in some of their hats, the clay pipes, and the carbide lamp on the mine wagon. The men on the left appear to be resting their feet on a compressed-air pipe.

Frank Warne (b. 1901) worked underground with candles like these:

They were made of what they call a tallow candle – green, with a fairly big wick on them. Used to buy 'em in a bunch, you know, thirty hanging on a bunch, and you used to just pull 'em off, you see.[7]

These underground men wore flannel shirts and jackets called 'slops' made of material called 'Rushin' Duck', which was 'like a very fine canvas'. It would swell with the wet and was very tough wearing. The trousers were also known as 'Ducks'.[8] Several men are wearing 'Yorks' below the knee. Sidney French remembered that a pair of working boots cost 9/9d at this time.[9] The man in the bowler hat, fifth from the left, was the mine blacksmith, and the man on the extreme right in the long overcoat was the mine captain.

This adit was the scene of a dramatic accident when the men tapped through into old workings flooded with water. Fortunately nobody was injured. Sidney French, who worked on Dartmoor mines from 1903 to 1913, was an eyewitness to this event:

I can't tell 'ee what year it happened. It was in my time, you know. It was when I worked up there . . . Well, Harold Jory and an old man called Sowden, us was there working, and we were out having our lunch, or crib as we called it . . . We were in the Dry where us used to dry our clothes. We heard something, and I was the first one to jump up and get to the door. And when I opened the door . . . the water was going down. And us had great poles there, oh, so big around as meself, what us used to put in in underground as timber where it was soft ground . . . [It] washed they away, yes.[10]

Elsie Bellamy, whose father was John James Coaker, captain of the mine, remembered him sending a telegram to London after the accident, saying the men would be off work for a few days.[11]

This was the only adit at Golden Dagger Mine. It has since been destroyed by forestry operations, but the foundations of the Dry can still be seen.

From left to right, the men in the photograph have been identified as follows:

1. *Frank Rensfield* (not local)[12]

2. *Johnny (Jack) Wills* of Ashburton[13]

3. *Bill Crout (??)* of Buckfast[14]

4. *William Jory* (1877–1927), son of Captain Richard Jory of Vitifer. He took over from his father as captain of Vitifer Mine for a time before moving in about 1916 to Clitters Mine, Gunnislake and then to Kit Hill, where he died in 1927 aged fifty. His wife was Bessie White, the daughter of a Postbridge farmer[15]

5. *Harry Earling (? sp.)*, the mine blacksmith. He was not a Postbridge man[16]

6. *George Coaker* of 'Cape Horn' (see plate 38). He was the brother of John James (no. 11) and first cousin to George (no. 9)[17]

7. *Charlie Rowlands.* He was an orphan from Plymouth, brought to Postbridge by a Mr Balkwill (? sp.). He died in Postbridge in about 1968[18]

8. *Unknown*, but came from Ashburton[19]

9. *George Coaker* of Postbridge, the son of Jonas Coaker of Pizwell[20]

10. *Sam Withycombe* of Postbridge[21]

11. *John James Coaker* (1873–1913). The son of John Coaker of 'Cape Horn', he was always known as 'John James' (see figure 4). Like other Postbridge men he had worked for a time at Owlacombe Mine near Ashburton. His wife was Mary Jory, the daughter of Richard and Anna Jory of Vitifer. At the time this photograph was taken he was captain of Golden Dagger Mine. He died at Dinah's House in 1913 at the age of forty, suffering from pneumonia, which was a common complaint among miners.[22]

Plate 40 *Stamps water-wheel at Golden Dagger Mine, c.1912*
Photographer: Chapman & Sons (no. 11938)
Grid reference: SX 68348012
Original given to Author by Mrs Winnie Murch, 1977

This wheel was one of the broadest in use on Dartmoor, measuring 22½ ft × 9 ft (6.9 m × 2.7 m) (Hamilton Jenkin 1974, p.106). The pit in which it was housed can still be seen and measures internally 24 ft 6 in. × 11 ft 4 in. (7.47 m × 3.45 m). Its purpose was to create the power to drive sixteen head of Cornish stamps (plate 41) which were installed in the adjoining shed. It appears to have been a pitchback wheel.

Plate 41 *Cornish stamps at Golden Dagger Mine, c.1912*
Photographer: Chapman & Sons (no. 11939)
Grid reference: SX 68348012
Original loaned by R. Bellamy

This shows the stamping machinery which was housed inside the shed seen in plate 40. It gives a good impression of the scale of some of the water-powered machinery to be found on a moorland tin mine.

The stamps axle turned by the water-wheel of plate 40 can be clearly seen. It has projecting cams which engaged in sequence with vertical lifters (seen behind the axle) thus raising the stamp heads and letting them drop on to the tin ore, crushing it to a fine sand. The holes of oval section in the stamps axle were used for retrieving broken cams, which were themselves set in holes of rectangular section. The horizontal strips at the bottom of the boxes into which the crushed material fell could be removed if access was needed for repair or cleaning.[23]

The man in the photograph has not been positively identified but it is possible that he is George Soper, who was in charge of the stamps at Hexworthy Mine in about 1900[24] and later, but still before the First World War, at Golden Dagger. It is remembered that he was literally deafened by the noise the stamps made, which is hardly surprising given the quantities of galvanized sheeting surrounding them.[25]

At Vitifer Mine the man in charge of the stamps was John Dawe of Higher Lydgate, Postbridge. He was an old man when Sidney French knew him working there. There were two shifts for the stamps men: 7 a.m.–5 p.m. and 5 p.m.–7 a.m.[26]

Note the massive sawn timbers and the grease at the end of the axle.

Plate 42 *Round buddle at Golden Dagger Mine, c.1912, looking north-north-west*
Photographer: Chapman & Sons (no. 11942)
Grid reference: SX 68398015
Original loaned by Miss Annie Sleep

The round buddle was introduced on Dartmoor in the mid-nineteenth century and was a means of preliminary concentration of tin ore after it had been crushed under the stamps. A wooden launder leads to the top of the central buddle cone or 'spreader'. The crushed material would be shovelled into this launder and mixed with a stream of water. This would then spread over the central cone and settle out in the buddle proper. While this was happening, the gearing that can be seen above the cone, powered by a small water-wheel, drove several 'sweeps' that have been removed before this photograph was taken (but see plate 57). These sweeps rotated round the buddle with a motion similar to that of the arms in a modern sewage works. They were made of wood and

had pieces of rag or thin sacking hanging below them. Their purpose was to create riffles in the deposit building up on the buddle floor so that the heavier good-quality tin would have something to catch against and would not be washed away with the surplus water and waste. Also they helped to build up an even deposit without any runnels in it.

A deposit of concentrate would be built up to a maximum depth of 10–12 in. (250–300 mm) and would then be tested for quality by the tin dresser using a vanning shovel. On the basis of this test two lines would be circumscribed through the deposit to divide it into three grades – heads, middle-heads and tails. The heads consisted of the heaviest, best-quality tin forming the ring nearest the central cone, the middle-heads formed the middle ring, and the tails were the poorest-grade outer ring, usually discarded as waste.[27]

The boys in the picture are digging out the three grades. The outer ring or tails has been virtually removed by the boy on the right, while the left-hand boy has his shovel in the middle-heads (or middles) and the other has his in the heads.

The three buddle boys are, from left to right:

1. *Reginald Coaker*, son of Captain 'John James' and grandson of Captain Richard Jory of Vitifer. His sister Elsie Bellamy told me that he was killed by a sniper on the way home from the First World War, at the age of nineteen.[28] The poignancy was echoed, less accurately but equally forcefully, by Annie Sleep:

That's Reggie – he was killed in the First World War –
went all through the war, him and another cousin of mine fought together all through the war, and they was killed in the very last battle.[29]

2. *Sidney Warne*, son of 'Cranky' George Warne of Kings Oven. He too was killed in the First World War, in its early stages.[30]

3. *John Withycombe*, son of Sam Withycombe (see plate 39). He moved away from Postbridge to a farm in Staffordshire where he died in about 1969.[31]

The site of this buddle can still be identified, on the west side of the track leading to Dinah's House, but it is now much overgrown and marshy.

Notes and References to Plates 38–42

1 An almost identical photograph, showing the men in slightly different positions, was given the same serial number by Chapman & Sons. It has been published by James Mildren (1984, p.42)
2 Oral inf., W. Withycombe, 6 Jan. 1971 (tape)
3 Oral inf., Miss Annie Sleep, 10 Aug. 1970
4 Oral inf., Miss Annie Sleep, 21 Dec. 1973; Mrs Elsie Bellamy, 18 July 1976
5 Oral inf., Sidney French, 4 Feb. 1974 (tape)
6 *Idem*
7 Oral inf., Frank Warne, 30 Oct. 1973 (tape)
8 Oral inf., John Hamlyn, 5 July 1973 (tape); Mrs Polly Osborn and Mrs Agnes Evely, 2 Aug. 1979; *et al.*
9 Oral inf., Sidney French, 7 Nov. 1974
10 Oral inf., Sidney French, 4 Feb. 1974 (tape)
11 Oral inf., Mrs Elsie Bellamy, 18 July 1976
12 Oral inf., Miss Annie Sleep, 10 Aug. 1970 (tape); Sidney French, 4 Feb. 1974 (tape)
13 Oral inf., Sidney French, 4 Feb. 1974 (tape)
14 Oral inf., Bill Warren, 31 Aug. 1972
15 Oral inf., Mrs Winnie Murch, 6 Nov. 1976. This man may in fact be Harold Jory, brother to William

16 Oral inf., Sidney French, 4 Feb. 1974 (tape)
17 Oral inf., Miss Annie Sleep, 10 Aug. 1970 (tape)
18 *Idem* and Reginald Warne, 20 May 1975
19 Oral inf., Sidney French, 4 Feb. 1974 (tape)
20 Oral inf., Miss Annie Sleep, 10 Aug. 1970 (tape); John Hamlyn, 23 April 1974
21 *Idem* and Sidney French, 4 Feb. 1974 (tape)
22 Oral inf., Miss Annie Sleep, 10 Aug. 1970 (tape); Mrs Elsie Bellamy, 18 July 1976; *et al.*
23 Oral inf., William Grose, 1 Aug. 1981
24 W. A. Grose *in litt.*, 11 Dec. 1977
25 Oral inf., Mrs Elsie Bellamy, 14 Sept. 1970
26 Oral inf., Sidney French, 17 Dec. 1975
27 The above account is a summary of several descriptions of the buddling process, especially that by Frank Warne, 30 Oct. 1973 (tape), and Donald Smith, 16 Aug. 1984 (tape). For historical accounts of buddling, see Earl (1968) and Burt (1982)
28 Oral inf., Mrs Elsie Bellamy, 18 July 1976
29 Oral inf., Miss Annie Sleep, 10 Aug. 1970 (tape)
30 *Idem*
31 *Idem*

Plate 43 *Dinah's House and Redwater valley, c.1927*
Photographer: D. Smith *Grid reference:* SX 685800 (viewpoint)
Original loaned by D. Smith

This view is looking north-westwards upstream to the site of the by now abandoned water-wheel and stamps of Golden Dagger Mine.

In the foreground are some 3½ in. (89 mm) steel pipes formerly belonging to Dartmoor Tin Mines Limited and which Donald Smith, engineer, found extremely useful for his new projects.[1]

Plate 44 *View north-north-east upstream to the engine house and Birch Tor, c.1927*
Photographer: D. Smith *Grid reference:* SX 685797 (viewpoint)
Original loaned by D. Smith

Challacombe Down is visible on the right.

A good view of the workings, engine house and dressing floors. Birch Tor in the distance. On the right can be seen the three large trommel classifiers mounted on steel pontoon which the Dartmoor Tin Mines Co. experimented with before I came. They used the big gas engine to supply current to the motors driving suction pumps. The project was a failure but I made good use of much of the gear they left behind.[2]

The trommels (described in plate 51) are *in situ* and were connected to a 5 in. (127 mm) suction pump powered by a 45 volt generator. Dartmoor Tin Mines Limited intended to flood the valley and suck the material from the floor.[3]

Plate 45 *View southwards from the engine house looking down the Redwater valley, c.1926*
Photographer: D. Smith
Grid reference: SX 68557993 (viewpoint)
Original loaned by D. Smith

The gantry in this picture carried a pipe which brought water to a water-wheel set below it. The wheel then powered rods which drove the sweeps for a round buddle.[4] Compare with plates 55 and 56.

Plate 46 *View northwards up the Redwater valley, with ponies in the foreground, c.1927*
Photographer: D. Smith   *Grid reference:* SX 685797 (viewpoint)
Original loaned by D. Smith

Sheds for buddles can be seen behind the ponies. In the words of Donald Smith, 'Ponies were a constant nuisance'.[5]

Another distraction was caused by the arrival of Miss Beatrice Chase of Widecombe, who started talking to the men. As Donald Smith relates:

She came down there and was talking to one of them and I said, 'I'm sorry, but I can't allow you to talk to my men.' 'Oh, why not? Why can't I talk to them? I'm not doing any harm.' I said, 'Yes, but he's doing harm by not working . . . He's causing trouble there and probably costing us pounds in loss of tin.' 'Oh, I can't see he's losing tin.' I said, 'Well, I'm afraid he is. If you'd like to come up to the engine house, I'll explain that to you.' Well, she did come up there and she chatted and she said, 'Oh well, I'm very pleased to have come to see you. I'll come and see you again.' . . . She looked like one of these Georgian types. She used to wear silk pantaloons and silk stockings, you know, like a footman would wear, you know, one of the old-fashioned footmen. Oh she was a caper – a character. We heard all sorts of stories about her.[6]

Plate 47 *Alluvial ore-bearing ground in the Redwater valley being dug out, c.1926*

Photographer: D. Smith   *Grid reference:* SX 684800
Original loaned by D. Smith

Dinah's House can be clearly seen in the background.

The four men were among several from Plymouth who were found work at Golden Dagger Mine. The material they are digging out was put in the wagons, which carried it to sluices for preliminary sorting. The wagon or skip on the left could be turned in any direction, unlike the side-tipping variety in plate 50. These wagons came from one of the 'shiny ore' mines in the Hennock/Lustleigh area, according to Gilbert Warne, an employee at Golden Dagger.[7]

The man second from the left had to be sacked by Donald Smith for threatening Panchaud, the manager, with a shovel. After this incident Panchaud acquired a dog for his protection.[8] Third from the left is a man called Maclaughlin, and the man on the right was called Tucker.[9]

Plate 48 *View northwards up the Redwater valley to*
Dinah's House, c.1927
Photographer: D. Smith *Grid reference:* SX 685795 (viewpoint)
Original loaned by D. Smith

This shows how the ground was excavated on both sides of the tramway before being taken for washing through the sluices.[10]

Plate 49   *Two men from Plymouth working at the sluice
head, c.1926*[11]
Photographer: D. Smith
Original loaned by D. Smith

Plate 50 *Long sluice with tailings pit, c.1926*
Photographer: D. Smith
Grid reference: SX 685795 (approx. viewpoint)
Original loaned by D. Smith

This view, looking up the valley towards Dinah's House, shows one of Panchaud's experiments with a series of long launders or sluices designed to catch the tin in stages, with the waste flowing on to a tailings pit at the bottom. Panchaud had learnt this technique in the tinfields of Nigeria.[12]

The side-tipping wagon was one of the old Vitifer Mine skips.[13]

Plate 51 *A trommel designed by Donald Smith, in operation c.1927*
Photographer: D. Smith *Grid reference:* SX 685799
Original loaned by D. Smith

A trommel was essentially a large revolving sieve with internal projecting pegs for preliminary sorting of material to a size suitable for washing in sluices, buddles, etc. Inside the trommel were three concentric hollow steel cylinders with a spindle running through the centre. Each cylinder had a different mesh – 1 in., ¼ in. or ¹⁄₁₆ in. (25, 6 or 1.6 mm). When rotated, the trommel caused the turf and loose material to be beaten into a slurry before passing through the graded screens. The resulting product was then fed directly to a round buddle. This was the first electrically powered trommel that Donald Smith devised. It was driven by a 3 h.p. electric motor.[14]

Plate 52 *Developed form of trommel, c.1928*
Photographer: D. Smith *Grid reference:* SX 685799 (approx.)
Original loaned by D. Smith

This developed form of trommel unit used a small conveyor belt to remove waste. The same unit can be seen in the centre of plate 56. Note the multi-pronged stone fork on the left – stones could not roll off it easily and it allowed water to drain through.[15]

The view is looking northwards, up the Redwater valley.

Plate 53 *Developed trommel units in the lower part of the Redwater valley, c.1929*
Photographer: D. Smith   *Grid reference:* SX 688790 (approx.)
Original loaned by D. Smith

This view is looking northwards to Challacombe Down.

These two trommel units side by side with buddles attached could be moved up the valley on pipes resting on rails which could be progressively taken up and placed ahead. The worked ground behind could then be filled with waste stone and tailings.

Donald Smith planned to use several of these units side by side working up the valley, and obtained a quotation for ten of them, the parts being supplied by Frederick Braby & Company of Bristol. H. J. Cattaneo, chairman and one of the directors of Torr Trust Limited, was keen to have twenty of them, but the closure of the mine in 1930 prevented any expansion, despite the fact that the units were found to be the most effective method of working the deposits.[16]

Plate 54 *Round buddles under construction, c.1927*
Photographer: D. Smith   *Grid reference:* SX 689791 (approx.)
Original loaned by D. Smith

This photograph appears to have been taken near the bottom end of the Redwater valley, looking south-west to the bulk of Grendon Common and Ephraim's Pinch. Note the water-wheel for power. The small buddle on the left was for treating heads, i.e. the best-quality concentrate, before it was carted to the dressing-floors by the engine house.[17]

Plate 55 *View to the engine house from the west, c.1926*
Photographer: D. Smith   *Grid reference:* SX 685799
Original loaned by D. Smith

This shows the site of buddles and a shelter for the Wilfley and Borden concentration tables. Donald Smith had the latter working under Flewin, Panchaud's predecessor, but Panchaud did not use them.

Wilfley and Borden tables were both types of shaking-table. The Wilfley table was slightly inclined and had oblique riffles on its surface. The Borden table was bumped on straps. Both required a continuous stream of concentrate to operate efficiently and Donald Smith never used them when he was in charge. Panchaud too felt they were unsuitable, and sold the Wilfley table.[18]

A good view is given of the engine house, which was wooden-framed with corrugated iron. It included a covered workshop, producer gas plant, engine room, separator room, office and tin store, concentrate drier and the dressing-floors (at the right-hand end of the building).[19]

It is probably Ernest Webb tending the buddle and two men from Plymouth tramming. Donald Smith remembers that the pipe in the left foreground froze then burst one evening just as he was passing underneath: 'It was like a cannon shot'.[20]

Plate 56 *View north-eastwards over buddles to the engine*
          house, c.1927
Photographer: D. Smith   *Grid reference:* SX 685799
Original loaned by D. Smith

This shows well the impact of the workings and machinery on a moorland landscape. To appreciate the scale, note the cluster of human figures in the centre. Note also on the right the pipe gantry and water-wheel that were visible in plate 45.

The water-wheel on the left powered the sweeps of the round buddle in the foreground. The buddle is in the process of being dug out – a deposit of rich tin is visible against the central cone (cf. plate 42). The buddle has a 'tailings race' around it to allow quicker cleaning. The tailings could be washed straight to settling-pits.[21]

The trommel illustrated in plate 52 can be seen between the buddle and the group of men.

Plate 57 *Round buddle at lower workings, c.1927*
Photographer: D. Smith   *Grid reference:* SX 685797(?)
Original loaned by D. Smith

In Donald Smith's words, 'Good view of buddle showing sweeps and the launder feeding over the centre head and the concentrate building up.' Redvers Webb is on the extreme right, feeding the buddle.[22]

Plate 58 *Cleaning out a buddle, c.1927*
Photographer: D. Smith   *Grid reference:* SX 685799
Original loaned by D. Smith

This is another view of the buddle illustrated in plate 56, but seen here from the other side. Donald Smith described the scene as follows:

> *Redvers Webb cleaning out a buddle built just below the first workings – Note type of barrow used. We made all our own barrows. One special big barrow we made as a bit of a joke for Fred Warne and he loaded it with 12 sacks of cement and pushed it from Dinah's cottage to the engine house! We made all our waterwheels too. Five waterwheels and two raff wheels altogether.*[23]

A raff wheel would raise water to a higher level.

Plate 59 *Tin dressing-floors at Golden Dagger Mine, c.1927*
Photographer: Woman friend of Panchaud
Grid reference: SX 68557990
Original loaned by Miss Mortimore

These floors were attached to the bottom end of the building known as the engine house.

The large tub in front of the three men is a chimming-kieve and in front of that is a square buddle. The kieve was not normally in that position but had been moved there for the photograph so that Jim Webb (on the right) could stand beside it with a packing-bar as if he was working. For a description of the kieving process see plate 27.

In the foreground is a vanning shovel laid across a small kieve. The vanning shovel was an essential tool of the tin dresser for testing the quality of the tin concentrate. This smaller kieve is sitting on a chimming-floor, part of which can be seen in the extreme left-hand corner of the photograph. The floor was at a lower level so that water could quickly drain away when the kieves were emptied. Two piles of concentrate can be seen beside the head of the square buddle. Just visible on the extreme right is a heather brush which was used in the square buddle to produce shallow riffles against which the heavy tin could settle. Above the square buddle is a wooden launder attached to the side of the shed. The pipe leading from it carried water to the buddle.[24]

On the left is C. A. Panchaud, mining engineer and local manager of the mine when the photograph was taken. He had succeeded Mr Flewin in 1926 and was himself replaced by Donald Smith in 1927. Donald Smith is standing in the centre, aged twenty-one and responsible at the time for the engines and electrical plant. The tin dresser, Jim Webb, is on the right.

Jim Webb (1862–1951) was the son of a miner, Tom Webb. His mother was an Anderson. He was a miner all his life and had worked abroad in gold mines, besides Hexworthy, and Wheal Friendship at Marytavy. The house he built for himself at Postbridge in 1907 – Tor View – is now occupied by the daughter of Harry Warne. Jim Webb is mostly remembered as a tin dresser, though for a time before the First World War he was in charge at Golden Dagger Mine. He married the sister of John James Coaker. Among places where he lived was Caroline, now an abandoned dwelling about half a mile (700 m) west-north-west of the Warren House Inn. Donald Smith recalls that he made a strange whistling noise through his nose, and understands that this was the result of working with arsenic in the Marytavy mines.[25]

Plate 60 *Petter engine at Golden Dagger Mine, c.1927*
Photographer: Unknown from Newton Abbot
Grid reference: SX 68557990
Original loaned by D. Smith

This shows the Petter 36 h.p. semi-diesel twin-cylinder oil engine in the engine house. In December 1925 Donald Smith travelled to the mine with a man called Penny, the works engineer from Petters of Yeovil, who was overseeing the installation of this engine. It replaced a much more powerful gas engine.

Note the air bottle and pump on the left, and the lubricating oil filter on the right. The belt on the right was used to drive the electric generator during very dry weather. At other times the generator was coupled to the water turbine. The magnetic separator was behind the partition wall.

The generator, the turbine and the magnetic separator were all brought from Vitifer Mine, where they had previously been used.[26]

Plate 61 *Horse and cart transferring tin concentrates to the dressing-floor, c.1927*

Photographer: D. Smith   *Grid reference:* SX 68557990
Original loaned by D. Smith

After we had developed the lower workings and buddles we were able to produce concentrates good enough to be taken direct to the dressing floors and worked on the square buddle. We transferred these by using a horse and cart hired from Jack Withycombe [of Soussons Farm] and we were able to tip right onto the dressing floor. Jim Webb and his son Redvers in photo.[27]

Fernley Warne (b. 1907) of Modbury remembers that the cart was made by Wadmans of Throwleigh.[28]

Plate 62 *Lorry for transporting tin to Princetown railway*
         station, c.1929
Photographer: D. Smith   *Grid reference:* SX 685799 (approx.)
Original loaned by D. Smith

This shows Petherwicks' lorry from Princetown being loaded with bags of tin concentrate to be sent away for smelting. The 'Penryn' Metal Company supplied the bags for the tin. When Donald Smith first went to Golden Dagger each bag was about 2 ft 6 in. (0.76 m) long and about 8 in. (0.2 m) wide, and held 3 cwt of tin, but during his time there smaller bags came into use, each holding 1 cwt.[29] Many people remember the weight of the tin and their surprise on seeing such small bags inside the horse-drawn carts used originally. Frank Hodge commented:

> *Five of they in the cart make a horse tug his guts out to come up over Oakery Hill and that, you know. And you'd look over the tail-board and there were these little sacks. You'd think anybody could pick 'em up, but you couldn't, you know. They was heavy.*[30]

The men in the photograph are, from left to right: Harry Warne, the lorry driver, Jim Webb, Redvers Webb and an unknown lad from Postbridge.[31]

Plate 63 *Mixing concrete for the pipe to the newly installed turbine, c.1927*

Photographer: D. Smith   *Grid reference:* SX 68557990
Original loaned by D. Smith

This scene is in front of the engine house in virtually the same spot as that shown in plate 64. The upper section of the pipe where the pressure was low was made out of Coalas tar drums.[32]

Plate 64 *Jim Webb, the tin dresser, outside the engine house, c.1927*

Photographer: D. Smith   *Grid reference:* SX 68557990
Original loaned by D. Smith

He is standing on the road to Dinah's House, outside the engine house. The barrels in the background contained semi-diesel oil for the Petter engine.[33]

Plate 65 *Jim Webb, Donald Smith and T. Redvers Webb, c.1927*

Photographer: Unknown   *Grid reference:* SX 68537988
Original loaned by D. Smith

Jim Webb, the tin dresser, was the highest-paid employee after Donald Smith and Panchaud, earning £2.5s per week, which Donald Smith was later able to increase to £2.10s. The other men earned £2 per week, apart from Freddy Warne, who received £2.2s, later increased to £2.5s, and Redvers Webb, who also got an increase to £2.2s. Panchaud received £6 per week, and Donald Smith £3 (increased to £3.5s when he took over).[34]

T. Redvers Webb, the son of Jim Webb, was born at 'Cape Horn' in 1901 and died in 1967 aged sixty-six.[35] Donald Smith described both father and son as 'fine characters'.

Barely visible behind the men is a round buddle used for concentrating heads. This was situated below the engine house and dressing-floor, and can be seen on the right of plate 55. The view is up the valley, and the dressing-floor shed is out of the picture on the right. Note the managerial tie worn by Donald Smith, the waistcoats of Jim and Redvers Webb and the 'Yorks' that Jim Webb has tied below his knees.

Plate 66 *Group outside the entrance to Dinah's House,*
1927
Photographer: Unknown   *Grid reference:* SX 68478003
Original loaned by Miss Mortimore

This photograph was taken at some time during 1927 before the Plymouth men came to work on the mine. Donald Smith recalls that it was probably a Saturday, when the wages were paid. Several other local people who were employed at the time do not appear in the photograph as they had gone home. It is not known who took the picture but the camera used belonged to Ernest Webb.[36]

Dinah's House is a structure at least nineteenth century in origin. It was in a dilapidated condition when Sidney French first went mining in 1903, and it was refurbished then. It was lived in by various families of miners at different times, including both the Coakers and the Jorys before the First World War. It was last occupied in 1942 by Mrs Harry Warne. Besides being known as Dinah's House, it was also variously called Dinah's Cottage, Dinah's Bungalow or just plain Dinah's. The origin of the name is unknown.[37]

Donald Smith described it as follows:

It was a very nice well built bungalow consisting of five rooms with a big room below, which we used as a storeroom for equipment etc. I built a garage beside the bungalow and also put in a water closet when Panchaud was manager. I lived in the cottage with the Flewins – the first manager and his Dutch wife – during the winter 1925–6.[38]

When you went in the door you went straight ahead to an office, and left to a lounge. There were two bedrooms on the right separated by a corridor from the kitchen, which was over the storeroom.[39]

The substantial ruins of the house can still be seen today and were recently consolidated by the Dartmoor National Park Authority.

Identifications are as follows:[40]

Standing from left to right
1. Mrs Harry Trude
2. Donald Smith
3. Walt Somerfield
4. Gilbert Warne
5. Redvers Webb
6. Harry Warne
7. Harry Trude with his son Brian
8. Dick Perryman (?)
9. Ernest Webb
10. Jimmy Webb
11. William Webb

Seated from left to right
1–3. Three female relatives and friends of Panchaud, plus his dog Tor.
4. C. A. Panchaud

Plate 67 *Group of Plymouth workers, c.1927*
Photographer: D. Smith   *Grid reference:* SX 684800
Original loaned by D. Smith

These were four of the dozen men from Plymouth who joined the work-force at Golden Dagger. The tall man, third from left, was called Maclaughlin and lived with his wife and baby in the old Golden Dagger Dry (SX 68298032), which is now reduced to ruins.[41]

Dinah's House can be seen in the background on the right, and the old Golden Dagger stamps on the left.

Plate 68 *Group of workers outside the dressing-floors shed, c.1927*

Photographer: D. Smith   *Grid reference:* SX 68557990
Original loaned by D. Smith

This photograph should be compared with plate 39 to see how much working dress, and presumably attitudes, had changed within a period of only fifteen years but including the First World War. Notice especially the hats and cigarettes which so clearly reveal the period.

Standing from left to right[42]
1. Jim Webb
2. Unknown from Plymouth
3. Unknown from Plymouth
4. Redvers Webb
5. Unknown from Plymouth
6. Ernest Webb
7. Maclaughlin

Front row, left to right
1. Harry Warne
2. Unknown from Plymouth
3. Unknown from Plymouth

Plate 69 *Men on work party to repair the mine leat, c.1927*
Photographer: D. Smith
Original loaned by D. Smith

3. Freddy Warne and his dog Vick
4. Bill Webb
5. Gilbert Warne (with binoculars)
6. Jim Warne

The Birch Tor & Vitifer Mine Leat, which also supplied Golden Dagger Mine, was approximately seven miles (11 km) long, having two branches taken off the East Dart and the North Teign rivers above Postbridge. Donald Smith records, 'This group were working well up on the moor above Postbridge cleaning out the old leat and repairing breaks'.[43] Identifications are the following, from left to right:

1. Ern Webb
2. Alex (Jock) Shaw

Alex Shaw was a Scotsman who came to work at Bellever Farm when Galloway cattle were introduced for the first time. He lost his job there and worked for Donald Smith, who remembers him as 'a good worker, clever with mechanical gear'. William Webb (b. 1902) and Ern Webb were the sons of John Webb, who was killed in the First World War. Gilbert Warne (b. 1910), Freddy's son, first went to work at Golden Dagger in 1924, earning 7/6d per week. He now lives in Princetown.[44]

Notes and References to Plates 43–69

1 D. Smith *in litt.* rec'd 5 Nov. 1983
2 *Idem*
3 Oral inf., D. Smith, 16 Aug. 1984
4 D. Smith *in litt.* rec'd 5 Nov. 1983
5 *Idem*
6 Oral inf., D. Smith, 16 Aug. 1984 (tape)
7 Oral inf., Gilbert Warne, 4 Oct. 1983
8 D. Smith *in litt.* rec'd 5 Nov. 1983
9 Oral inf., Gilbert Warne, 4 Oct. 1983
10 D. Smith *in litt.* rec'd 5 Nov. 1983
11 *Idem*
12 *Idem* and oral inf., 16 Aug. 1984 (tape)
13 Oral inf., Gilbert Warne, 4 Oct. 1983
14 D. Smith *in litt.*, 8 March 1978, *in litt.* rec'd 5 Nov. 1983, and oral inf., 16 Aug. 1984 (tape). For further information on trommels, see Burt (1982, pp.32–5)
15 D. Smith *in litt.* rec'd 5 Nov. 1983
16 *Idem* and oral inf., 16 Aug. 1984 (tape)
17 D. Smith *in litt.* rec'd 5 Nov. 1983
18 Oral inf., D. Smith, 16 Aug. 1984 (tape). See also Earl (1968, pp.89–90) and Burt (1982, p.63 and plate 3)
19 D. Smith *in litt.*, 8 March 1978
20 D. Smith *in litt.* rec'd 5 Nov. 1983
21 *Idem*
22 *Idem*
23 *Idem*

24 D. Smith *in litt.*, 12 Feb. 1978 and 8 March 1978
25 Oral inf. from numerous persons but especially Frank Warne, 30 Oct. 1973 (tape); Sidney French, 4 Feb. 1974 (tape); Mrs Brook, 26 Sept. 1973; D. Smith, 16 Aug. 1984
26 D. Smith *in litt.* rec'd 5 Nov. 1983
27 *Idem*
28 Oral inf., Fernley Warne, 11 June 1984
29 D. Smith *in litt.* rec'd 5 Nov. 1983 and oral inf., 16 Aug. 1984
30 Oral inf., Frank Hodge, 29 Dec. 1972 (tape)
31 D. Smith *in litt.* rec'd 5 Nov. 1983
32 *Idem*
33 *Idem*
34 Oral inf., D. Smith, 16 Aug. 1984 (tape)
35 Oral inf., Mrs Eva Webb, 22 Feb. 1974; D. Smith *in litt.* rec'd 5 Nov. 1983
36 D. Smith *in litt.*, 20 Feb. 1983
37 Oral inf., Sidney French, 7 Nov. 1974; Mrs Elsie Bellamy, 18 July 1976; Mrs Winnie Murch, 6 Nov. 1976; Mrs Brook, 21 Jan. 1983
38 D. Smith *in litt.*, 12 April 1978
39 Oral inf., D. Smith, 26 May 1983
40 Oral inf., Mrs Brook, 21 Jan. 1983; D. Smith *in litt.*, Feb. 1983; oral inf., Gilbert Warne, 4 Oct. 1983
41 D. Smith *in litt.* rec'd 5 Nov. 1983
42 D. Smith *in litt.*, 7 Aug. 1985
43 D. Smith *in litt.* rec'd 5 Nov. 1983
44 Oral inf., Gilbert Warne, 7 Sept. 1971 and 4 Oct. 1983; D. Smith *in litt.* rec'd 5 Nov. 1983

Plate 70 *View northwards up the Redwater valley, c.1935*
Photographer: Unknown
Grid reference: SX 681800 (viewpoint)
Copy loaned by S. Timms *ex* C. Warren Collection

This photograph was taken from Soussons Down looking northwards up the valley to the buildings of Vitifer Mine. It gives a good impression of how large water-wheels appeared when viewed from a distance in a wide moorland landscape. Birch Tor is on the extreme right. Soussons Down is now covered with commercial coniferous afforestation planted in the 1940s, so it is not possible to compare this scene today. The photograph illustrates what we might have been left with had there been a more enlightened policy towards abandoned structures and machinery on the open moor.

In the foreground is the stamps water-wheel of Golden Dagger Mine and directly behind it is that of Vitifer Mine.

75

Plate 71 *Abandoned stamps water-wheel at Golden*
Dagger Mine, 26 September 1937
Photographer: P. H. G. Richardson
Grid reference: SX 68348012
Negative loaned by P. H. G. Richardson

Compare with plates 40 and 41. This shows clearly
how toothed wheels were used to transmit the power
of the water-wheel to the stamps axle.

Plate 72 *Remains of wooden buddle at the lower end of the Redwater valley, 26 September 1937*
Photographer: P. H. G. Richardson
Grid reference: SX 689791 (approx.)
Negative loaned by P. H. G. Richardson

This is almost certainly the remains of one of the mobile buddles attached to the developed trommel units that Donald Smith designed and built for working in sequence up the valley (see plate 53).

The method of construction of the buddle can be clearly seen. Skilful carpentry was required to make it watertight. Donald Smith recalls that he bought timber by the truckload from a Plymouth firm. He would obtain 1000 ft (304 m) of 6 in. × ¾ in. (152 mm × 19 mm) prepared deal. He could buy 100 ft (30.5 m) of 3 in. × 2 in. (76 mm × 51 mm) timber for 7/6d if prepared or 3/6d if just sawn. It came in 12–14 ft (3.7–4.3 m) lengths.[1]

Plate 73 *Tin dressing plant set up by Mr Olver, in operation at Golden Dagger, 26 September 1937*
Photographer: P. H. G. Richardson
Grid reference: SX 685799 (?)
Negative loaned by P. H. G. Richardson

Mr Olver and a man called Thicknes (? sp.) extracted some tin at Golden Dagger in the 1930s. Mr P. B. Spencer Stanhope, who had been one of the directors of Torr Trust Limited, the company working Golden Dagger when Donald Smith was there, seems to have provided the support for this operation. In 1931 Stanhope entered an informal partnership with Mr K. Fox of Natsworthy. Mr Fox recalls a bizarre luncheon at Dinah's House in the mid-1930s, consisting largely of 'bully beef and red wine', which was served by Stanhope to a gathering of Duchy officials meeting there to discuss the future of the mine.[2]

So it seems that Olver was the last person to work tin for a living on Dartmoor. He lived in Dinah's House. Peter Richardson visited him in November 1938 and was told that the mine was about to restart in earnest and that £2000 had been spent on preliminary work. According to Olver, a company was preparing to spend £50 000 on working the alluvial deposits and development underground.[3] On this optimistic but unfulfilled note some 800 years of documented tinworking on Dartmoor came to an end with the outbreak of the Second World War, as Olver was killed in action in France.[4]

Bill Withycombe, the local postman, said of him:

Things weren't very bright for him, you know, like outlook for work and that. He worked hard there to try and make it go, you know. He joined the army, you see, and he got killed out in France. He was a very nice fellow.[5]

Plate 74 *Harry Trude, former tin miner, explaining the*
workings of a round buddle, 22 September 1971
Photographer: Author   *Grid reference:* SX 68547988

Harry Trude was born on 3 June 1900, found work at the Postbridge mines in 1918 and was employed there for most of the 1920s. He remembered that at one time they were off work for six weeks because of frost, and it was during this period that he and a friend, Jim Collins, caught forty rabbits one night on Hameldown, with the help of a dog called Sago. They paunched them and the following day managed to strap them to a Dunelt motorcycle and negotiate the snowy roads to Moretonhampstead, where they sold them for one shilling each.[6]

Harry also planted many of the first trees at Fernworthy and Bellever, something which he regretted in later years: 'although I helped to plant them, the point is they're a blot on the landscape'.[7] He married a girl from Moretonhampstead in 1924. Many will remember him working in the East Dart Hotel in the early 1970s and living then in the bungalow above Lower Merripit called Sunnymead. He died in 1979.

Plate 75 *Donald Smith at the entrance to Dinah's House, 26 May 1983*

Photographer: Author   *Grid reference:* SX 68478003

Notes and References to Plates 70–75

[1] Oral inf., D. Smith, 16 Aug. 1984 (tape)
[2] Oral inf., K. Fox, 18 July 1983
[3] Private papers in possession of P. H. G. Richardson, 'Recent Information Vol. 1 1927–1952'
[4] M. Radford *in litt.*, 20 Jan. 1974, *et al.*
[5] Oral inf., W. Withycombe, 6 Jan. 1971 (tape)
[6] Oral inf., H. Trude, 19 Sept. 1969 and 3 July 1970 (tape)
[7] Oral inf., H. Trude, 3 July 1970 (tape)

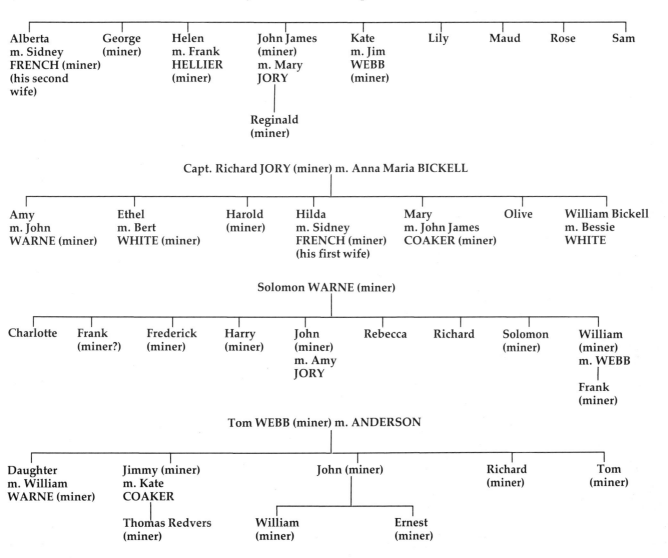

John COAKER of 'Cape Horn'

Alberta m. Sidney FRENCH (miner) (his second wife)	George (miner)	Helen m. Frank HELLIER (miner)	John James (miner) m. Mary JORY	Kate m. Jim WEBB (miner)	Lily	Maud	Rose	Sam

Reginald (miner)

Capt. Richard JORY (miner) m. Anna Maria BICKELL

| Amy m. John WARNE (miner) | Ethel m. Bert WHITE (miner) | Harold (miner) | Hilda m. Sidney FRENCH (miner) (his first wife) | Mary m. John James COAKER (miner) | Olive | William Bickell m. Bessie WHITE |

Solomon WARNE (miner)

| Charlotte | Frank (miner?) | Frederick (miner) | Harry (miner) | John (miner) m. Amy JORY | Rebecca | Richard | Solomon (miner) | William (miner) m. WEBB |

Frank (miner)

Tom WEBB (miner) m. ANDERSON

| Daughter m. William WARNE (miner) | Jimmy (miner) m. Kate COAKER | John (miner) | Richard (miner) | Tom (miner) |

Thomas Redvers (miner)

William (miner)   Ernest (miner)

Figure 4 *Simplified chart of some Postbridge families showing the impact of mining on a community*

81

GLOSSARY

Adit/Adit level horizontal tunnel driven into the side of a hill for drainage and access.

Air compressor machine producing compressed air for rock drills and ventilation.

Alluvial used to describe ore-bearing material washed from one place and deposited in another, usually the bottom of a valley. This process mostly took place in remote geological periods but at Vitifer and Golden Dagger the deposits included waste material from earlier workings.

Black tin tin ore ready for smelting after it has been crushed and cleaned. Usually contains between 60% and 70% tin metal.

Blast furnace furnace for smelting tin where the forced draught is supplied by bellows.

Borden table shaking-table for concentrating crushed tin ore.

Buddle rectangular (square buddle) or circular (round buddle) pit for concentrating crushed tin ore.

Californian stamps late nineteenth century improvement on traditional Cornish stamps (q.v.) whereby the stamp head twisted as it fell.

Cam shaped iron piece set in and projecting from the stamps axle in order to raise lifters (q.v.).

Captain title given to the man in charge of operations on the mine.

Carbide lamp lamp using acetylene gas generated by mixing water with carbide granules.

Centre head central cone or spreader in a round buddle which enabled even distribution of the concentrate.

Chimming method of concentrating crushed tin ore in wooden tubs called kieves.

Chimming-floor wooden floor on which chimming-kieves were set.

Chimming paddle implement with which the concentrate in a kieve was stirred.

Classifier device for sorting tin concentrate into grades.

Concentrate crushed tin ore reduced to a fine sand.

Cornish stamps massive iron blocks, often in sets of four, powered by a water-wheel and used for crushing tin ore.

Crib meal break for miners.

Downright hatch device for turning water off a water-wheel.

Dresser man in charge of the cleaning of the crushed ore.

Dressing-floor(s) where crushed ore is cleaned and separated from associated waste material to produce tin concentrate.

Dry building with boiler where underground clothes could be dried.

Ducks name given to trousers worn by underground miners.

Dues money paid to the owner of mineral rights as a proportion of the value of ore raised.

Dynamite high explosive used for blasting underground.

End furthest point at which miners were working in an underground level.

Engine house usually refers to a steam engine but used at Golden Dagger in the 1920s to refer to a building containing various items of machinery including gas and semi-diesel engines.

Fathom unit of length equal to 6 ft (1.8 m).

Forenoon morning. Used especially in 'forenoon shift', 7 a.m.–3 p.m.

Hatch device for controlling the flow of water, usually in a leat.

Head (of stamps) used to describe the number of individual stamp heads powered by one water-wheel, e.g. twelve head of stamps.

Headframe erected over shafts as support for winding apparatus, etc.

Heads best-quality tin concentrate produced in buddles, etc.

Hydraulic classifier device using water and gravity for sorting tin concentrate into grades.

Kieve wooden tub in which crushed tin ore was concentrated.

Kittle broth common breakfast among miners, consisting of bread and hot water (or tea) in a basin with a lump of butter.

Launder artificial wooden gutter for carrying water, usually to a wheel.

Lease right granted by a landowner or mineral owner to work for tin.

Leat channel or gutter, sometimes several miles long, dug in the ground and bringing water from a stream or river to a mine.

Leat embankment final part of a leat where it is carried on to an embankment before being transferred to a launder to take it to a water-wheel.

Level see *Adit level*.

Licence right to work for tin, granted by the landowner or the owner of mineral rights.

Lifter wooden beam or thick iron rod with iron stamp heads attached at the base. Raised by coming into contact with cams (q.v.).

Lode vein of metallic ore in rock.

Magnetic separator device consisting of moving belts and magnets for separating iron, e.g. specular haematite, from tin.

Middle heads/Middles middle grade of tin concentrate produced in buddles, etc.

Mill structure where water-powered machinery was used for crushing/grinding, e.g. a stamping-mill.

Openwork opencast excavation along the line of a tin lode, usually medieval in origin.

Ore (tin) tin-bearing mineral.

Packer (mechanical) device for automatically beating the sides of a kieve to concentrate the crushed ore.

Packing-bar iron bar used for manual beating of the side of a kieve.

Pelton wheel water-powered turbine for generating electricity. A large volume of water falling from a considerable height is directed through a small-diameter nozzle against bifurcated buckets attached to the rim of a disc.

Pitchback used to describe a water-wheel where the water hits the wheel at approximately one o'clock, causing it to rotate in the same direction as an undershot wheel.

Pithead surface machinery, etc., associated with a shaft.

Producer gas gas produced as a fuel by burning special coal in a heating stove. At Golden Dagger Mine the gas was used to power an engine generating electricity.

Pumping rods rods taken off the crank of a water-wheel and used for transmitting a reciprocating motion to operate pumps within a shaft.

Race the outflow channel from a water-wheel or buddle.

Raff wheel small wheel used for raising water or liquid concentrate to a higher level.

Reverberatory furnace furnace for smelting tin where the heat is reflected on to the ore.

Round buddle circular pit used for concentrating tin ore.

Rushin' Duck name given to the material of which miners' underground clothes were made.

Season pudding sort of pasty containing potato, onion and meat which could be boiled.

Semi-diesel thin oil used in the Petter engine.

Separator see *Magnetic separator.*

Sett area of land comprising the limits of a mine.

Shaft vertical or inclined tunnel for mining purposes.

Shiny ore micaceous haematite, a type of iron ore.

Skiddy bag leather 'gaiter' worn by miners below the knee.

Skip mine truck or wagon on rails.

Slops name given to the jackets worn by underground miners.

Sluice device like a long launder used for preliminary sorting of alluvial ore-bearing material.

Smelting-house where tin concentrate (black tin) was reduced to tin metal (white tin) in a furnace (blast or reverberatory).

Sollar wooden platform underground.

Spreader central cone of a round buddle, used for even distribution of the concentrate.

Square buddle rectangular pit for concentrating crushed tin ore.

Stamping-mill water-powered complex where tin ore was crushed.

Stamps ore crushing machinery in the form of drop hammers powered by a water-wheel.

Stamps axle extended axle of a water-wheel with projecting cams (q.v.) for engaging the lifters of the stamps.

Stope piece of ore-bearing ground being worked by underground miners either above (overhand) or below (underhand) the level.

Streamwork tin-bearing alluvial deposit in valley bottom worked by miners.

Stull wooden platform underground.

Sweeps revolving arms in a round buddle with pieces of rag or sacking attached to them to create riffles and an even deposit of the concentrate.

Table slightly inclined rectangular piece of wood with riffles on its surface and given a jolting motion by an eccentric drive, for concentrating crushed tin ore.

Tailings lowest grade of tin concentrate after buddling, etc., usually discarded as waste.

Tailings race outflow channel from round buddle for speedy removal of waste.

Tails see *Tailings.*

Tappet projecting arm or part of a machine designed to engage with another thus transmitting power.

Timberman man employed in placing timber supports underground.

Tin usually used to describe the ore (cassiterite – SnO_2) but also the concentrate (black tin) and metal (white tin).

Tin dresser see *Dresser.*

Toregg salted dried cod.

Tramroad light railway for mine trucks carrying ore, usually from the adit level to the stamps.

Trommel revolving sieve for preliminary sorting of ore.

Turbine small wheel driven by water under pressure for generating electricity, e.g. a Pelton wheel.

Vanning shovel special shovel for testing the quality of tin concentrate.

Vein lode (of tin).

Wagon mine truck on rails, for carrying ore.

Wheelpit pit in which a water-wheel turns.

Wilfley table shaking-table for concentrating tin ore.

Winding gear machinery for raising ore from a shaft.

Yorks piece of string or leather strap tied below the knee to keep the bottom of the trouser leg out of the mud.

BIBLIOGRAPHY

Atkinson, M. *et al.* 1978 *Dartmoor Mines – The Mines of the Granite Mass.* Exeter Industrial Archaeology Group.

Barton, D.B. 1967 *A History of Tin Mining and Smelting in Cornwall.* Truro: Bradford Barton.

Blake, W.J. 1915 Hooker's Synopsis Chorographical of Devonshire. *Rep. Trans. Devonshire Ass.* **47**, 334–48.

Booker, F. 1967 *The Industrial Archaeology of the Tamar Valley.* David & Charles.

_____. 1970 Industry. In Gill, C. (ed.) *Dartmoor: A New Study*, pp.100–138. David & Charles.

Broughton, D.G. 1968/9 The Birch Tor & Vitifer tin mining complex. *Trans. Cornish Inst. Engrs*, **24**, 25–49.

_____. 1971 The Land Half Made. In *Kingston Geol. Rev.* Res. Seminar Issue no.2, vol.1, no.6, pp.1–25.

Burt, R. 1982 *A Short History of British Ore Preparation Techniques in the 18th and 19th Centuries.* Aalst-Waalre: De Archaeologische Pers Nederland.

Burt, R. *et al.* 1984 *Devon and Somerset Mines.* University of Exeter.

Chugg, B. 1975 *Victorian and Edwardian Devon from Old Photographs.* Batsford.

Collins, J.H. 1912 *Observations on the West of England Mining Region.* Plymouth.

Cook, R.M.L. *et al.* 1974 Eylesbarrow (1814–1852) – a study of a Dartmoor tin mine. *Rep. Trans. Devonshire Ass.* **106**, 161–214.

Court, L.H. 1927 *Some Dartmoor Saints and Shrines.* London: Morgan & Scott.

Crossing, W. 1912 *Guide to Dartmoor*, 2nd edn. Plymouth: Western Morning News.

Dines, H.G. 1956 *The Metalliferous Mining Region of South-West England*, vol.2. H.M.S.O.

Earl, B. 1968 *Cornish Mining.* Truro: Bradford Barton.

Greeves, T.A.P. 1980a An outline archaeological and historical survey of tin mining in Devon, England, 1500–1920. In Wächtler, E. & Engewald, G.–R. (eds) *ICOHTEC Int. Symp. Ges. Bergbaus und Hüttenwesens (Freiberg)*, **1**, 73–89.

_____. 1980b A history of Whiteworks Tin Mine. Part 1: 1790–1848. *Plymouth Mineral & Mining Club J.* **11**(2), 11–16.

_____. 1981a The archaeological potential of the Devon tin industry. In Crossley, D.W. (ed.) *Medieval Industry* (CBA Res. Rep. no.40), pp.85–95.

_____. 1981b *The Devon Tin Industry 1450–1750: An Archaeological* and Historical Survey. Unpublished Ph.D. thesis, University of Exeter.

_____. 1985a The Dartmoor tin industry – a simple guide to the field remains. *Devon Archaeology*, **3**.

_____. 1985b Steeperton Tor Tin Mine, Dartmoor, Devon. *Rep. Trans. Devonshire Ass.* **117**.

Grinsell, L.V. 1978 Dartmoor barrows. *Proc. Devon Archaeol. Soc.* **36**, 85–180.

Hamilton Jenkin, A.K. 1974 *Mines of Devon Volume 1: The Southern Area.* David & Charles.

_____. 1981 *Mines of Devon: North and East of Dartmoor.* Exeter: Devon Library Services.

Harris, H. 1968 *Industrial Archaeology of Dartmoor.* David & Charles.

Hemery, E. 1983 *High Dartmoor – Land and People.* Robert Hale.

H.M.S.O. 1958 *Catalogue of Plans of Abandoned Mines other than Coal and Oil Shale.* H.M.S.O.

Le Messurier, B. (ed.) 1966 *Crossing's Dartmoor Worker.* David & Charles.

Major, J.K. & Watts, M. 1977 *Windmills and Watermills from Old Photographs.* Batsford.

Mildren, J. 1984 *Dartmoor in the Old Days.* Bodmin: Bossinney Books.

Minchinton, W. 1974 *Devon at Work: Past and Present.* David & Charles.

Pilkington-Rogers, C.W. 1930 *Days on Dartmoor.* Methuen.

Raistrick, A. (ed.) 1967 *The Hatchett Diary.* Truro: Bradford Barton.

Reid, C. *et al.* 1912 *The Geology of Dartmoor.* H.M.S.O.

Richardson, P.H.G. 1972 Hexworthy Tin Mine. *Plymouth Mineral & Mining Club J.* **3**(3), 3–4.

_____. 1973 Hexworthy Tin Mine. *Plymouth Mineral & Mining Club J.* **4**(2), 11–13.

Robins, J. 1984 *Follow the Leat*, 2nd edn. Published privately.

Smith, J.H.D. 1983 *IPM Catalogue of Picture Postcards and Year Book 1983.* Dorking: IPM Publications.

Somers Cocks, J. 1970 The Forest Boundary. In Gill, C. (ed.) *Dartmoor: A New Study*, pp.277–81. David & Charles.

Somers Cocks, J. & Greeves, T. 1983 *A Dartmoor Century 1883–1983: One Hundred Years of the Dartmoor Preservation Association* DPA Pub. no.8.

Spooner, G.M. & Russell, F.S. (eds) 1967 *Worth's Dartmoor.* David & Charles.

Williams, J. 1870 *The Cornwall and Devon Mining Directory.* London.

INDEX

Numbers in bold indicate plates.